Heav[illegible]
Under Your Feet
Pregnancy for Muslim Women

Umm Hasan bint Salim

Ta-Ha Publishers Ltd.

First Published January 2009

Published by
Ta-Ha Publishers Ltd.
Unit 4, The Windsor Centre,
Windsor Grove, London, SE27 9NT
Website: www.taha.co.uk
E-mail: sales@taha.co.uk

Written by: Umm Hasan bint Salim
General Editor: Dr. Abia Afsar-Siddiqui

A catalogue record of this book is available from the British Library.

ISBN-13: 978 1 84200 092 2

Cover image by: Saleha Atewala
Book design and typeset by: Open Squares Ltd.
Printed and bound by: Mega Basim, Turkey

This book is not intended to replace the services of trained health professionals, or be a substitute for medical advice. You are advised to consult with your healthcare professional with regard to matters relating to your health, and in particular regarding matters that may require diagnosis or medical attention.

To Allah belongs the dominion of the heavens and the earth.
He creates what He wills.
He gives to whom He wills females,
and He gives to whom He wills males.
Or He couples them as males and females,
and he renders whom He wills childless.
Indeed, He is Knowing and Capable.

(Surah Ash-Shura 42:49-50)

Contents

Foreword

Among the countless bounties from Allah that we enjoy in every moment of our lives, there is one special bounty that transforms human beings in a most extraordinary manner. That bounty is the special gift of *rahmah* (compassion) that causes parents to cherish the life of their newborn above that of their own lives. Allah says that He has created the womb and from His own name of *Al-Rahman* (The Most Compassionate) He has derived a name for the womb calling it *rahm* and whosoever maintains the bond of the womb, He will maintain His bond with them (Abu Dawud). On account of that status the parent-child bond remains one of the most powerful forces in nature.

Whilst we enjoy this bounty of becoming a parent, it is also necessary to recognise parenthood as a gift from Allah with responsibilities that will last a lifetime. Being cognisant of the spiritual aspects of parenthood is equally important as the need for adequate medical attention during pregnancy and birth.

We are all, as the Prophet ﷺ said, shepherds (Bukhari) with responsibility for our flock. Living as we do in a world that presents an increasing array of challenges to the survival of faith in the hearts of the generations to come, we need to be vigilant, in the spiritual sense, during the crucial stages of early development and throughout the tender years of their lives. Our children's spiritual life will depend on the nourishment they receive from us. If they are nourished with love for Allah and His Prophet ﷺ and reverence for the Qur'an, then *iman* (faith) will blossom in their hearts and Islam will adorn their deeds.

This book, written by our dear sister Umm Hasan, is a gallant and sincere effort at helping Muslim mothers and fathers along the awe-inspiring journey into parenthood. I pray that Allah accepts her work and through it kindles *noor* (the light of guidance) in the tender hearts of our children for generations to come. *Ameen.*

Shaykh Riyad Nadwi
Oxford, UK

Preface

Pregnant with my first child, I looked to friends, family and books for advice during this very special time. I needed support and the assurance that everything I was going through was normal. My main source of comfort came from books. Books informed me of what to expect and told me what to do and what not to do. They even helped make my pregnancy real when I didn't have a bump to show for it!

Despite this, I found that most books were written by non-Muslim women, for non-Muslim women. Many issues I wanted answers for were not discussed. None of them told me when an angel would visit the new being inside me to write its destiny and to grant it a soul. Some books were filled with obscene pictures that I could not look at myself, never mind share with my husband!

More importantly, there was a spiritual void in these books. My pregnancy was a time when I wanted to draw closer to Allah ﷾, our Creator and Sustainer, but these books talked about pregnancy fashion dos and don'ts. Sometimes, I had nothing other than my new baby on my mind and I had to transform this mental addiction to fit in with my purpose in life: to worship Allah ﷾, as He has told us in the Qur'an:

> *And I have not created jinn and men except that they should worship Me.* (Surah Adh-Dhariyat 51:56)

Alhamdulillah, we have lots of Islamic literature on what comes before pregnancy and all that comes after it, but there is very little to be found on pregnancy itself. I therefore wrote this book to join other *Muslimahs* in beginning to fill this gap. *Insha'Allah*, this book will support the expecting Muslim woman and aid her journey through this wonderful phase in life.

The adopted approach is one that appeals to the modern-day Muslim woman: a focus on contemporary and scientific issues, balancing them with an Islamic emphasis. Everyday, real-life situations faced by pregnant women are discussed whilst ensuring that our spiritual needs, and that of our babies, are the foremost considerations.

I have divided the book into three sections. Beginning with a focus on ourselves, the first section on "You" discusses the thought processes of pregnant women, the adjustment to pregnancy, our experiences and how we cope. The second section, "Your Baby", turns the spotlight on to the new person inside us, contemplating a mother-to-be's concerns and considerations for the best start in life. The final section covers the moment we all (very anxiously) wait for, "Labour and Birth", and centres on the last stretch of these nine months, including its preparation and process, with some discussion of the immediate aftermath.

Though this book has been endorsed by a Muslim midwife, Sofia Odugleh, and written in consultation with Muslim GPs, my intention is not to replace medical advice. This is something I leave to the doctors and midwives. As this is not a guide to pregnancy as such, I also avoid discussing in detail how you and your baby change with each stage of pregnancy. There are many excellent books that are available on such issues.

This book is also not a substitute for all the issues we need to consult an *'alim* (scholar in Islam) about. There are several such issues in pregnancy, for example fasting in *Ramadan* and post-natal bleeding, that many pregnant women will need to consult a trustworthy scholar about. I have tried to avoid presenting a collection of legal rulings in this book and sincerely urge all women to speak to those qualified to answer our questions when it comes to such issues. We can contact the local mosque, or telephone Islamic institutions across the country, or even worldwide.

I ask Allah ﷻ to make my efforts beneficial for all those who come across this book and for it to be a source of mercy for me.

Acknowledgements

All praise is for Allah ﷾, the One and Unique, the Creator and Originator. To Him is due all gratitude. All good is from Him, and Him alone, and all mistakes are from myself.

When I told my dad that I wanted to write a book, he thought, "This daughter of mine is finally going to *do* something with that Oxford degree of hers!" and he stopped trying to convince me to do a doctorate. I thank my parents for encouraging me to actually go ahead and write this book, reflecting their support and encouragement throughout my life. Mum, thanks for phoning me everyday and remembering every now and then to ask if I'm actually bothering to write anything!

As for my dearest husband, words cannot capture what I would like to convey here. I pray that Allah ﷾ rewards you with nothing less than the highest heights of Paradise.

I would like to express deep gratitude to my teachers, Shaykh Riyad Nadwi and Shaykh Akram Nadwi for their time, direction and inspiration over the years. You have both had invaluable input into this book. I am particularly grateful to Shaykh Riyad for his support and for the irreplaceable years with Dar al-Ulum Oxford that have shaped me into the woman I am today. Many, many thanks also to Shaykh Akram for his effort and patience in checking every *hadith* contained in this book.

A big hug to my dearest sister, Aapa; many, many thanks to Alima Ali for her help with this book; and to Afia Mufti, you've always been inspirational. A very, very special thank you to Amaal Vadakul, who not only thought of the title but was indispensable in driving this book to completion!

A thank you to GPs Henna Ehtisham, Salma Mughal, and Nosheen Jilani in particular for all their time and advice, and last but not least, a huge thank you to our very own midwife Sofia Odugleh for all her professional guidance and assistance.

I pray that Allah ﷻ accepts my efforts and grants me the ability to keep my intention behind writing this book sincere, firm and pure. *Ameen.*

I.
You

Congratulations, you're pregnant!

Alhamdulillah, we have been blessed with the gift of a new baby growing inside us and our *du'a*s (prayers) have been answered. Many of us treasure the memory of that positive result on the pregnancy test and the feelings we had when we first discovered we were expecting a baby. From that day on, we have never been the same again.

Pregnancy is not merely a physical process that is limited to our bodies. Pregnancy is also a mental and emotional journey filled with excitement, anxiety, happiness and lots of questions. Expecting a baby is a time of immense psychological change and preparation. This is when we begin the lifelong journey of motherhood.

Every mother to be, Muslim or not, wants only the best for her child. Every woman knows that this is not just about giving them the best pushchair and clothes, or the best milk, or the best toys. It is also about giving them the best mum there can be. This does not come with a few shopping sprees. Instead, what is needed is a recipe of *du'a*, dedication and effort, all of which the mother can begin with when pregnant.

This is why many pregnant women often realise that these special nine months are the ultimate time to turn to Allah ﷻ. We vow to take this time to reform and improve ourselves. As mothers-to-be, we become acutely aware of how our children will learn from us as soon as they meet us. This may not be how we have thought about it, but this is the time for us to embark on a journey of self-rectification as essential preparation for the grave responsibility awaiting us.

Becoming a Mother

"Clearly, deciding to have children is not a particularly rational decision and if we really sat down and calculated the financial burden, the heartache and the sleepless nights, then most people would probably decide against reproduction."[1]

This amusing quote is sadly a manifestation of the thought processes of many women today when contemplating having children. Ganley continues, "So why does it continue to be the choice that the majority will make?" Though Ganley leaves us with no answer to her interesting question I'd like us to ask ourselves, why did we want to become a mother?

Many of us do not capture our desire to become pregnant as "wanting to become a mother". Instead we may have said, "I want to have a baby". Wanting to be a mother sounds dull, tiresome and full of responsibility, whereas babies are cute and adorable! Perhaps, this is the first time we have thought of ourselves as mothers-to-be, even though we know that we are carrying a baby!

Whether or not this is the first time we have thought of the prospect of becoming mums, addressing this question of why we decide to be mothers is essential as it is synonymous with the *intention* we form in becoming mothers. The intention of becoming a mother is of paramount importance because:

> The reward of deeds depends upon the intentions and every person will get the reward according to what he has intended.
> *(Bukhari, Book of Belief)*

1 Ganley, J. (2004), *Becoming a Parent: The Emotional Journey through Pregnancy and Childbirth*, Wiley

It is in the light of this saying of the Prophet ﷺ that it is of vital import that we analyse our answers to the big question of why we decide to have children. Every minute of every day with our babies can hold potential rewards for us if we have the best of intentions. If our intention to have babies is one that Allah ﷻ is well pleased with then *insha'Allah* our pregnancy, our babies, and our lives with them, will bear fruit upon fruit. If this hope for the greatest rewards with our Lord is part and parcel of our intention in becoming mothers then we are treading the path to success.

Thus we have the answer to Ganley's question: why do the majority of women choose to have children? This is our *fitrah*. *Fitrah* is the natural disposition instilled in human beings by Allah ﷻ, and our *fitrah* is to worship Him.[2] Included in our *fitrah* is a need and want for family and a desire to reproduce. It is our *fitrah* to have children and to become mothers. This inherent need is described in a beautiful hadith, "Verily, heaven is found at her [mother's] feet",[3] where He has shown us that motherhood is more valuable than any job, more important than any course and is an integral part of our purpose in life. This role and reward of a mother is *insha'Allah* what we strive to fulfil in our intention to become mothers.

---

2 "Every newborn child is born in a state of *fitrah*. Then his parents make him a Jew, a Christian or a Fire-Worshipper, just as an animal is born intact. Do you observe any among them that are maimed (at birth)?" (Muslim, Book of Destiny)

3 Nasai, Book of Fighting in the Way of Allah

Magnificent Mum

During pregnancy we experience a renewed appreciation for our dearest mums. It is only now that we truly realise what our mothers have been through for us and only now do we begin to understand the status of motherhood. Allah ﷻ mentions motherhood, pregnancy and breastfeeding in the Glorious Qur'an:

> *We have enjoined on man kindness to his parents; in pain did his mother bear him, and in pain did she give him birth.* (Surah Al-Ahqaf 46:15)

> *And We have enjoined on man (to be good) to his parents. In travail upon travail did his mother bear him, and in two years was his weaning. Show gratitude to Me and to thy parents; to Me is thy final goal.* (Surah Luqman 31:14)

Allah ﷻ specifically refers to pregnancy and breastfeeding, mentioning them between two commands: 1) to be good to our parents; and 2) to show gratitude to Allah ﷻ together with gratitude to our parents. Our mothers endured the difficulties of pregnancy and loved us even before we entered this world. They bore hardship for us even before they met us. We are indebted to our parents in a similar way to how we are indebted to Allah ﷻ for all that we have. Just as we can never thank Allah ﷻ enough, we can also never repay our parents:

> A son does not repay what he owes to his father unless he buys him (the father) in case he is a slave and then emancipates him. *(Muslim, Book of Divorce)*

Abu Buraidah narrates that he was with Ibn 'Umar and a Yemeni man was making *tawaf* of the House carrying his mother on his back saying, "I am her humble camel where her camel would have gotten frightened I will not." Then he said, "O Ibn 'Umar! Do you think that I have repaid her?" He said, "No, not even for a single moan that escaped her during childbirth." *(Bukhari, A Code for Everyday Living, 1/62, Repaying the Parents)*

Often, especially if we are pregnant for the first time, when we think "parents" we think of our own mothers and fathers. Now, it is our turn to be the parent. We need to turn the tables and focus on *us* as the parents, rather than our own parents. Expecting a baby is not an isolated nine months in our lives, it is the beginning of the great journey of motherhood.

The magnitude of the responsibility of parenthood is awe-inspiring. This magnitude is not in terms of how much sleep we will sacrifice, how much money we will spend, how much time we will devote to our children and our pain and suffering for them, but it is the shaping of our children's faith:

Every child is born with a true faith (i.e. to worship none but Allah ﷻ alone or on the *fitrah*) but his parents convert him to Judaism or to Christianity or to a Fire-worshipper, as an animal delivers a perfect baby animal. Do you find it mutilated? *(Bukhari, Book of Funerals)*

In this saying of the Prophet ﷺ, we as parents are responsible for keeping our children on the *fitrah* and keeping them firm on the Straight Path. It is not something that children learn to do themselves, or that we leave solely in the hands of Allah ﷻ, with no effort on our part. This endeavour in raising good Muslim children can begin now, even before we have held our children in our arms. By strengthening our own character and developing in our faith we can strive in becoming better believers. We, as parents, can be role models for our children. Let our learning continue and grow in our pregnancy by utilising our time well, reading Islamic books and attending classes.

It is our duty to ensure our children develop to become sincere Muslims; a weighty responsibility, which we must now embrace and ask Allah ﷻ to help us with. We beg Allah ﷻ to make us amongst the best of parents.

A Whole New Bodily Experience

Pregnancy is an experience where no body part seems to go unscathed. After being unaware of the tiny being growing inside us, most of us are soon swamped by the colourful wave of symptoms that accompany early pregnancy. We quickly realise that our bodies are not their usual selves as we find ourselves making frequent dashes to the toilet and wanting to sleep all day. Welcome to pregnancy!

The physical changes in the first trimester often unsettle many of us. Consequently, the beginnings of a pregnancy can have a detrimental effect on our '*ibadah* (worship). We may find that we are busy being sick after the *Fajr* prayer instead of reciting Qur'an or we cannot concentrate as well on what we are reading. When it comes to *salah* (prayer), standing up too long or changing positions can make us feel dizzy and staying in *sujood* (prostration) can make us nauseous. Often, we simply have less time for '*ibadah* because we need to sleep more than usual, or we are less active than normal and everything seems to take a lot longer to do.

It might seem as though we are wasting time, being lazy or not achieving much because of these changes in our daily routine. It can be helpful to remind ourselves that this is quite normal, even expected. We are pregnant, not quite our usual physical selves and often not entirely "healthy". This is the one time we should really listen to our bodies and react to them accordingly. Let us not forget that it is not just ourselves that we need to look after, but that there is another tiny, highly dependent being forming inside us. Now there are two of us to care for.

We must sit down whenever we need to, and nap whenever we feel the need to as our bodies are demanding rest. We also need to eat what we like and leave what we do not like, as is the *sunnah*. So if the smell of chicken is nauseating, we shouldn't feel bad about not eating it! Our bodies are telling us what is good for us and what is not, so we ought to listen to them.

> The Prophet ﷺ never criticised any food (presented to him), but he would eat it if he liked it; otherwise, he would leave it (without expressing his dislike). *(Bukhari, Book of Virtues and Merits of the Prophet ﷺ and his Companions)*

At the same time, we are not "ill" and cannot excuse ourselves from *'ibadah*. Pregnancy is not an opportunity to slacken off in our worship. Instead, we need to aim for the exact opposite. Allah ﷻ has, *insha'Allah*, blessed us with nine continuous months for His remembrance through *salah*, without any breaks, thanks to not having a period. This is an opportunity not to be missed. Pregnancy is not an excuse from prayer. We can use pregnancy as a chance to make the effort to reform our souls, whilst maintaining a balance that is physically healthy for us.

Being pregnant is a time in our lives when we need Allah's ﷻ blessings in a way not known to us before. During pregnancy we are careful about how we strain ourselves physically and we watch what we eat and drink to avoid harming the new being inside us. Ultimately though, we rely on Allah ﷻ to get us, and our babies, through. Therefore, we need to do our part, in terms of worshipping Him and fulfilling our obligations, to help ensure Allah's ﷻ protection and mercy during our pregnancy. This is not the time to be forgetting Allah ﷻ. If we remember Allah ﷻ, we can be sure that He will remember us:

Remember Me - I will remember you, and be grateful to me and reject not faith. (Surah Al-Baqarah 2:152)

Improving Salah

Pregnancy is the only time where we are able to pray, non-stop, for nine whole months. This continuous praying can have one of two effects on our *salah*. It can be fantastic for those of us who feel that our *iman* and efforts suffer when menstruating and detrimental to those who benefit from a break in *salah*, as the feeling of returning to prayer refreshed and thirsty to stand before Allah ﷻ leaves us.

Some women feel that they manage to attain a level where their *salah* is more focused and fruitful when they have been praying regularly over several days or weeks. Then comes along the "dreaded" period and they find themselves having to start all over again in achieving a good level of concentration and satisfaction in *salah* once they resume praying. Menstruation is a natural reprieve granted to women and not an excuse to lapse, thus, pregnancy for such women is a golden opportunity to make sure they keep escalating and working towards perfecting prayer.

However, some find that they benefit from a break in *salah* whilst menstruating because it makes them appreciate prayer and purity, unlike when they are praying. They then itch to get back into *salah* whilst still on their period and their first week back into *salah* consequently consists of some of their best prayers. For such women, concentration in *salah* may not be optimal during pregnancy, as the beauty of *salah* is not revived in their breaks from praying.

For all of us, there are strategies we can employ in order to improve our prayer and develop *khushoo'* in *salah*. *Khushoo'* means submissiveness, calmness, serenity, tranquillity, dignity and humility. It is a focused state of mind and soul that many of us lack, or have trouble sustaining, during *salah*, despite Allah ﷻ having commanded us to have *khushoo'* in our prayers:

> *Guard strictly your prayers, especially the Middle Prayer; and stand before Allah in a devout (frame of mind).* (Surah Al-Baqarah 2:238)

Sadly, few of us fulfil this requirement regularly, if at all. Instead we may find ourselves fitting a dismal description given by the Prophet ﷺ:

> A slave may pray and have nothing recorded for it except a tenth of it, or a ninth, or an eighth, or a seventh, or a sixth, or a fifth, or a quarter, or a third, or a half. *(Abu Dawud, Book of Prayer)*

Or even worse:

> 'Umar ﷺ said, "A man might have white hair in Islam (i.e. reaches old age while Muslim), yet has not completed even one prayer for Allah, the Exalted!" He was asked, "Why is that?" He said, "He does not perfect the prayer's required *khushoo'*, solemness and attending to Allah with his heart." *(Ghazali, The Revival of the Religious Sciences, 10/202)*

We need to beg Allah ﷻ that we are not amongst such people and ask as the Prophet ﷺ used to ask:

اللَّهُمَّ إِنِّي أَعُوْذُ بِكَ مِنْ قَلْبٍ لاَ يَخْشَى

> "O Allah, I seek refuge with You from a heart that has no *khushoo'*." *(Tirmidhi, Book of Supplications)*

Alhamdulillah, lots of women also find that some of the *salah* they offer whilst pregnant are very focused and powerful. This is especially true if we use *salah* as a means of *du'a:*

> The closest that the slave can be to his Lord is when he is prostrating, so increase your *du'a* [at that time]. *(Muslim, Book of Prayers)*

> As for *sujood*, strive hard to make *du'a* in it, for it is bound to be answered for you. *(Muslim, Book of Prayers)*

Pregnant women have much to ask Allah ﷻ for and what better way to ask of Him than in *sujood* to Him? We can ask for whatever we like, from being blessed with a beautiful, healthy baby to an easy birth. One of the *du'as* which the Prophet ﷺ used to recite in his *sujood* was:

اَللَّهُمَّ اغْفِرْ لِي ذَنْبِي كُلَّهُ دِقَّهُ وَجِلَّهُ

"O Allah, forgive me my sins, the minor and the major."
(Muslim, Book of Prayers)

Some pregnant women feel moved to improve their *salah*, or to recite more than usual in their prayer. When realising our reliance on Allah ﷻ alone, when begging for His mercy and help, we may want to beautify our *salah* to really try and praise Allah how He should be praised. When seeking aid that none other than Allah ﷻ can provide we may want to try adding the following short and simple phrases that carry much weight:

In addition to saying, "Glory be to my Supreme Lord",[4] the Prophet ﷺ would also say "Perfect, Blessed, Lord of the Angels and the Spirit"[5] whilst in *ruku*. *(Muslim, Book of Prayers)*

Rifa'a ibn Rafi Az-Zuraqi رضي الله عنه said: "One day we were praying behind the Prophet ﷺ. When he raised his head, he said, 'Allah hears whoever praises Him'[6] and a man behind him said, 'Our Lord to You be much good and blessed praise.'[7] When he finished, he said, 'Who is the one who spoke?' The man said, 'Me.' He said, 'I saw thirty-odd angels rushing to see who would write it down first.'" *(Bukhari, Book of Characteristics of Prayer)*

4 سُبْحَانَ رَبِّيَ الْعَظِيمِ *Subhana Rabbi al-'Adheem* (Glory be to my Supreme Lord) said three times in Arabic whilst in *ruku*

5 سُبُّوحٌ قُدُّوسٌ، رَبُّ الْمَلَائِكَةِ وَالرُّوحِ *Subbuhun, Quddusun, Rabbul-mala'ikati war-ruh* (Perfect, Blessed, Lord of the Angels and the Spirit)

6 سَمِعَ اللهُ لِمَنْ حَمِدَهُ *Sami' Allahu liman hamidah (*Allah hears whoever praises Him)

7 رَبَّنَا وَلَكَ الْحَمْدُ حَمْدًا كَثِيرًا طَيِّبًا مُبَارَكًا فِيهِ *Rabbana wa laka'l-hamdu hamdan katheeran tayyiban mubarakan fih* (Our Lord to You be much good and blessed praise)

These are very easy to learn and implement in our *salah* yet they carry the power to revive our standing before The Almighty. They are but a small selection of many of the 'extras' we can add to our prayer.

Ramadan and Fasting

According to all four schools of thought, a pregnant woman is exempt from fasting only if she fears for the health of herself or her unborn child. Allah, The Merciful, has provided an exemption to fasting for such women. It is worth noting that simply being pregnant is not an excuse in itself to leave the fasts of *Ramadan*. So how do we know whether fasting will adversely affect our unborn? Should we be fasting?

For those of us asking ourselves these questions, there are two studies with Asian *Muslimahs*, conducted at a hospital in Birmingham, UK, that are of interest. The first study published in 1989 tracked the metabolic changes of eleven Asian pregnant women and compared them with a group of control mothers. The authors found that none of the fasting women had a completely normal set of biochemical values at the end of the fasting day but that there was no significant outcome on the pregnancy as compared with the control group. Nevertheless the authors stated that they would recommend the pregnant woman not to fast during *Ramadan*.[8]

The second study published in 1990 analysed the birth weights of 13,351 babies born at full term to Asian *Muslimahs* between 1964 and 1984 in comparison with two age-matched

8 Malhotra, A., Scott, P. H., Scott, J., Gee, H. & Wharton, B. A. (1989), British Journal of Nutrition, 61(3):663-72

control groups comprising white and non-Muslim Asian babies. The authors concluded that *Ramadan* had no effect on the mean birth weight of the babies born at full term regardless of when *Ramadan* occurred in the pregnancy.[9]

Further studies on the effect of *Ramadan* fasting in pregnant women on the birth weight of their babies have also been conducted in Iran,[10] Malaysia[11] and Yemen.[12] They have also reached the same conclusion; fasting in *Ramadan* does not result in low birth weight of the newborn. Therefore, healthy women with normal pregnancies do not risk their babies' health by fasting.

It is recommended that all pregnant women consult their health professional (preferably Muslim) prior to undertaking the fasts of *Ramadan*. Doctors can advise us best based on our health and pregnancy history, the length of the fasts and any other personally specific factors. We can also seek their advice on any precautions we may need to take when fasting and how best to fulfil our nutritional needs.

Pregnancy is a time when we want to do all that we can to benefit our souls and our baby. *Ramadan* is the perfect gift to aid this process, one that we should grasp with both hands whenever we can. Let us prepare for *Ramadan*, read up on its virtues, particularly the last ten days, and make the most of the month whilst we are pregnant as we have the unique opportunity to fast the entire month with no period to stop us!

---

9 Cross, J. H., Eminson, J. & Wharton, B. A. (1990), Archive of Disease in Childhood, 65:1053-6

10 Arab, M. & Nasrollahi, S. (2001), Medical Journal of the Islamic Academy of Sciences, 14(3):91-95

11 Salleh, H. (1989), Malaysian Journal of Reproductive Health, 7:69-83

12 Makki, A. M. (2002), Saudi Medical Journal, 23:1419-1420

Of course, if we are exempt from fasting then we should welcome this as a mercy and blessing from Allah ﷻ, and use it, particularly for the sake of the unborn. Pregnant women gain the rewards of fasting even if they do not do so, if and when they are exempt. Also remember that pregnant women do not have to fast if they are ill and a doctor has advised us not to fast, or if we are travelling, just like everyone else, but again, we must make up these fasts at a later date.

Another important point for pregnant women to bear in mind in *Ramadan* concerns sickness. If we are sick and the vomit exceeds a mouthful then this terminates the state of *wudhu*. However, we need to remember that unintentional vomiting does NOT break our fast. It is only if someone vomits intentionally, for example if someone sticks their fingers down their throat, which invalidates the fast. So if we are sick then we must continue the fast and we do not need to make up the fast at a later date.

A final issue for us during *Ramadan* regards giving blood, for example, for blood tests during antenatal appointments, or for checking haemoglobin levels in order to determine iron deficiencies. These do NOT nullify the fast and we can continue with such procedures whilst we are fasting.

As with other forms of worship and aspects of our *deen* (faith), during pregnancy we might not always be able to fulfil our aims and do as much as we would like to. We may not be able to concentrate as much and stand for as long as usual in prayer, we may be very inactive whilst fasting or need to sleep more than usual. Again, the important thing is to listen to our bodies, to do what we can and be good to ourselves. If we are not able to achieve as much as we did in our pre-pregnancy days then Allah ﷻ knows what we could have and would have done if we had the ability to do so and will reward us accordingly:

When a slave falls ill or travels, then he will get reward similar to that he gets for good deeds practiced at home when in good health. *(Bukhari, Book of Fighting in the Way of Allah)*

Abdullah bin 'Umar ﷺ said, "Allah's Apostle took hold of my shoulder and said, 'Be in this world as if you were a stranger or a traveller.'" The sub-narrator added: "Ibn 'Umar used to say, 'If you survive till the evening, do not expect to be alive in the morning, and if you survive till the morning, do not expect to be alive in the evening, and take from your health for your sickness, and (take) from your life for your death.'" *(Bukhari, Book to Make the Heart Tender)*

Hajj and 'Umrah

Pregnancy for many of us is a turning point in our lives when we sincerely hope and pray that we become better people and better *Muslimahs*, as we begin our journey of motherhood. If there were ever a sure-fire way to bring about this change in ourselves then visiting the House of Allah ﷻ would be it. The sense of being in a sacred state when in *ihram*, together with the majesty of the *Ka'ba* and being in its precincts as the guest of Ar-Rahman can catapult us into self-rectification and gives us the opportunity to begin motherhood as pure as the one we are carrying - sin free.

'Umrah is expiation for the sins committed (between it and the previous one). And the reward of *hajj mabrur* (the one accepted by Allah) is nothing except Paradise. *(Bukhari, Book of Minor Pilgrimage)*

While this may seem the ideal time to visit the House of Allah, there are some points that need to be considered before coming to a final decision. *Hajj*, in particular, is a spiritually, emotionally, physically and mentally demanding journey, crammed with millions of other people. Travelling when heavily pregnant or during early pregnancy, or if the pregnancy is at risk at any stage, is obviously not recommended. Even if we have a normal and healthy pregnancy, we need to be aware of the strenuous nature of the journey and that, should we need it, we may not receive the same medical attention that we are used to at home. Based on these cautions, some countries, such as Malaysia, do not allow pregnant women to go on *hajj*.

When considering *hajj* we need to speak to our health professionals about our intentions in terms of our own pregnancy and to receive simple travel advice to maximise the benefits of this journey, *insha'Allah*.

Emotional Changes

Pregnant women can be emotional wrecks. To put it mildly, most of us have a noticeable change in mood during pregnancy. Many women feel unusually sensitive, from being extra teary to being quick to anger. Being emotional is normal for us. A pregnant woman's progesterone level rises to ten times that pre-conception and we produce as much oestrogen in a single day as non-pregnant women produce in three years![13] Hormonal changes are partly responsible for our mood swings and so we should not be overly concerned about them. However, emotions are not purely hormone levels. As human beings we have a degree of

13 Stoppard, M. (1993), *Conception, Pregnancy and Birth*, Dorling Kindersley

control over our emotional states, with our ability to rationalise situations and our own perceptions. Therefore, the concern for us as Muslim women, especially as pregnant Muslim women, is how we react and deal with our emotions.

Emotion for the Muslim is not an irrational, uncontrollable human characteristic though it may be a natural one. Islam requires self-control and the regulation of emotion, so we need to strive in not letting these mood swings get the better of us. It is always important to maintain good character, even if we have the excuse of being pregnant! The value and importance of good character in Islam, whether or not we are pregnant, is captured in the following saying of the Prophet ﷺ:

> Among the best of you [are they] who have the best character. *(Bukhari, Book of Virtues and Merits of the Prophet ﷺ and his Companions)*

Not only is having good character important, we must also actively strive in avoiding the aspects of bad character that we experience as mothers-to-be. For example, the Prophet ﷺ placed a strong emphasis on controlling anger:

> A man said to the Prophet ﷺ, "Advise me!" The Prophet ﷺ replied, "Do not lose your temper." The man asked (the same) again and again and the Prophet ﷺ said each time, "Do not lose your temper." *(Bukhari, Book of Good Manners)*

There is particular wisdom in this advice for pregnant women. Research has shown the harmful effects of anger (as well as depression and anxiety) on newborns. Women that were more prone to anger had babies who had disorganised sleep patterns and did less well on measures of orientation, motor maturity and depression.[14] We can see that anger when pregnant can be detrimental to our babies so we should benefit from the advice of the Prophet ﷺ in how to curb it, as described in the saying of the Prophet ﷺ given above and also by using the following two remedies:

1. Saying the *ta'awwudh:*

أعُوذُ بِاللَّهِ مِنَ الشَّيْطَانِ الرَّجِيمِ

"I seek refuge in Allah from *Shaytan* the accursed."

> Sulayman ibn Sard رضي الله عنه said, "I was sitting with the Prophet ﷺ when two men abused each other and one of them became so angry that his face became swollen and changed. The Prophet ﷺ said, "I know a word that will cause him to relax, and this is, 'I seek refuge with Allah from *Shaytan*, the accursed.' (If he says these words) his anger will cool down." *(Bukhari, Book of Beginning of Creation)*

2. Making *Wudhu:*

> Verily, anger is from the devil, the devil was created of fire, and fire is extinguished only with water; so when one of you becomes angry, he should perform ablution. *(Abu Dawud, Book of General Behaviour)*

As pregnant women we may be able to continue, if not excel, in our *'ibadah* yet the emotional changes we experience can render our efforts redundant if we fail in subjugating them under our control. Usually it is those around us, especially our nearest and

14 Field, T. et al. (2002), Journal of Obstetrics and Gynaecology, 22(3):260-6

dearest, who suffer the consequences of our mood swings. This is very often commendably met with great understanding on their part, excusing us for being pregnant. However, we need to realise that our negative mood is not healthy for our families, ourselves or our unborn. Furthermore, our treatment of others is something we cannot neglect, even when pregnant, as we see in the following saying of the Prophet ﷺ:

> The poor of my *'Ummah* would be he who would come on the Day of Resurrection with prayers and fasts and *Zakat* but (he would find himself bankrupt on that day as he would have exhausted his funds of virtues) since he hurled abuses upon others, brought calumny against others and unlawfully consumed the wealth of others and shed the blood of others and beat others, and his virtues would be credited to the account of one (who suffered at his hand). And if his good deeds fall short to clear the account, then his sins would be entered in (his account) and he would be thrown in the Hell-Fire. *(Muslim, Book of Virtue, Good Manners and Joining of the Ties of Relationship)*

Here the true weight of treating others well and of maintaining good character is clear. We must accompany the fulfilling of Allah's ﷻ rights over us with fulfilling the rights of others. It may be easy for us to think, "Well, I don't steal and I haven't hit or killed anybody", but the damage we can do with a sharp tongue, fuelled by our hyper-emotional state, can be equally grave. We have a strong and clear message about how we use language and our tongues from the Prophet ﷺ as he warned us: that "those who are in the habit of abusing people and using obscene and foul language" will be in Hellfire. (Muslim, Book Pertaining to Paradise, Its Description, Its Bounties and Its Intimates)

> A believer is not one who taunts or curses or acts indecently or speaks vulgar language. *(Tirmidhi, Book of Virtues, Good Manners and Joining Ties)*

> A Muslim is the one from whose hands and tongue other Muslims are safe. *(Tirmidhi, Book of Faith)*

It is worth noting how these sayings of the Prophet ﷺ define a Muslim, or a believer, as someone who refrains not only from wronging people with their actions, but also with their words. The Prophet ﷺ instructed us to be very careful with our tongues, especially as women. As emotional pregnant women this applies to us in particular! He told his most beloved wife, A'isha رضي الله عنها, to be kind and lenient with her words, even to those who were hurtful or abusive:

> Narrated by A'isha رضي الله عنها: "A group of Jews entered upon the Prophet ﷺ and said, 'As-samu-alaikum' (death be upon you). I understood it and said, 'Wa-alaikum as-samu wal-la'n (death and the curse of Allah be upon you).' Allah's Apostle said 'Be calm, O A'isha! Allah loves that one should be kind and lenient in all matters.' I said, 'O Allah's Apostle! Haven't you heard what they (the Jews) have said?' Allah's Apostle said, 'I have said (to them) 'And upon you!''" *(Bukhari, Book of Good Manners and Form)*

Of course, *alhamdulillah*, not everyone has problems controlling their anger and their tongues. Some of us, however, will find that we cry more easily and are quite sensitive in this respect. In contrast to anger, this is an attribute that we should all aim to cultivate in ourselves with regards to how we feel for Allah سبحانه وتعالى, His words, and those He loves because the Prophet ﷺ described tears as a mercy from Allah سبحانه وتعالى:

Narrated by Usama ﷺ: The eyes of Allah's Apostle ﷺ started shedding tears. Sa'd said, "What is this, O Allah's Apostle?" The Prophet ﷺ said, "This is the mercy which Allah has lodged in the hearts of whoever He wants of His slaves, and verily Allah is merciful only to those of His slaves who are merciful (to others)." *(Bukhari, Book of Patients)*

Abu Bakr ﷺ, the man whom the Prophet ﷺ chose as his closest companion, the first khalifah after the Prophet ﷺ, the one who will have the honour of entering *Jannah* from any one of its eight gates, is renowned for his shedding of tears. His daughter, A'isha ﷺ said of him: "Abu Bakr is a very soft-hearted man and he cannot control his tears" and she also related:

During his illness, the Messenger of Allah ﷺ said, "Order Abu Bakr to lead the prayer." I told the Messenger of Allah ﷺ that, "Indeed, if Abu Bakr stands in your place the people will not be able to hear him due to his (excessive) weeping." *(Bukhari, Book of Call to Prayers)*

Having tender hearts and eyes that shed tears in compassion is a true mercy from Ar-Rahman. So now that we may be feeling extra emotional, instead of something superficial like a soap opera setting off a stream of tears, let us use this opportunity to think of Our Lord and be of those who will find shade on the Day when there will be no shade but the shade of the throne of Ar-Rahman. The honour and mercy of being under the shade of Allah's ﷻ throne on this Day, the Day of Judgement, will be for those who remember Allah ﷻ when they are alone and cry before him;[15]

15 The Prophet ﷺ said Allah will give shade to seven (types of people) under His Shade (on the Day of Resurrection). (One of them will be) a person who remembers Allah ﷻ and his eyes are then flooded with tears. (Bukhari, Book of *Zakat*)

the Day when the sun will be brought only a mile above our heads and we will be standing in pools of our own perspiration.[16] We can try to be included in this special category of people by remembering Allah ﷻ, His favours upon us, the mercy He shows us, pondering over the verses of the Qur'an and the descriptions of Hellfire and Paradise, reflecting on our book of deeds and begging forgiveness from our Lord. May Allah, the Most Merciful, make our hard hearts porous to His words and guidance, to allow us to shed tears for His sake, and to perfect our character.

The Prophet ﷺ made particular *du'a* for good character:

اهْدِنِي لِأَحْسَنِ الْأَخْلَاقِ لَا يَهْدِي لِأَحْسَنِهَا إِلاَّ أَنْتَ

> "Guide me to good character, none guides to good character but You." *(Muslim, Book of Prayers)*

Let us seek refuge from aspects of bad character that may be aggravated when pregnant and ask Allah ﷻ to help us in perfecting our character.

---

16 I heard Allah's Apostle ﷺ saying: "On the Day of Resurrection, the sun would draw so close to the people that there would be left only a distance of one mile." Sulayman ibn Amir said: "By Allah, I do not know whether he meant by 'mile' the mile of the (material) earth or an instrument used for applying collyrium to the eye." The Prophet ﷺ is also reported to have said: "The people would be submerged in perspiration according to their deeds, some up to their knees, some up to the waist and some would have the bridle of perspiration" and, while saying this, Allah's Apostle ﷺ pointed his hand towards his mouth. (Muslim, Book Pertaining to Paradise, Its Description, Its Bounties and Its Intimates)

A Time for Patience

> *By time! Surely the human being is at loss. Except for those who have faith and do righteous deeds and exhort one another to truth and exhort one another to patience.* (Surah Al-'Asr 103:1-3)

There are times during pregnancy when we tell ourselves, or are told by others, to have patience, because whatever we are going through will soon pass. Patience with morning sickness, with digestive problems, with waking up every time we need to turn over in bed and, of course, in waiting for the baby!

Every woman finds that she is able to bear with patience some discomforts of pregnancy better than others. Equally, it is easy for every pregnant woman to get down about the bodily and emotional changes that we go through during pregnancy. *Alhamdulillah*, as Muslim women we have comfort in the fact that pain and suffering, distress and discomfort, be it the prick of a thorn, is a blessing in disguise as it purifies us from sin:

> No fatigue, nor disease, nor sorrow, nor sadness, nor hurt, nor distress befalls a Muslim, even if it were the prick he receives from a thorn, but that Allah expiates some of his sins for that. *(Bukhari, Book of Patients)*

These trying times when we find ourselves asking Allah ﷻ for patience are also times when we are shown His mercy. The most beautiful way in which we see this mercy as pregnant women is the effortless and free rewards we accrue: the good deeds we would normally have done or are in the habit of doing, but are now unable to do because we feel sick, or are too tired, or are just too big and heavy to do, are still recorded as having been done by us:

> When a slave falls ill or travels, then he will get reward similar to that he gets for good deeds practiced at home when in good health. *(Bukhari, Book of Fighting in the Way of Allah)*

This is the mercy of Ar-Rahman. We do not do a good deed and yet He still records the good deed for us! This is because Allah ﷻ knows that if He had given us the ability to do good, we would have surely done it, and that is enough for Him. *Alhamdulillah*!

We can also taste the mercy of the Most Merciful during difficult times by uttering a single sentence:

إِنَّا لِلَّهِ وَإِنَّـــا إِلَيْهِ رَاجِعُوْنَ

> *And give good news to the patient, who, when struck with disaster, say, 'Indeed we belong to Allah and to Him we will return.' Upon them be blessings from their Lord, and Mercy, and they are the rightly guided.* (Surah Al-Baqarah 2:155-7)

Allah ﷻ rewards those who have patience, those who say "Indeed we belong to Allah and to Him we will return" with a threefold reward of blessings, mercy and guidance. So every time we say these words, whether we feel sick or cannot reach the bottom of the shopping trolley because our bump gets in the way, we are rewarded in the best of ways. An excellent example of the best of rewards is with the wife of the Prophet ﷺ, Umm Salamah رضي الله عنها:

> Umm Salamah رضي الله عنها said: I heard the Messenger of Allah ﷺ say: "There is not one slave (of Allah) who is put through a trial and says: 'To Allah we belong, and to Him is our return; Oh Allah, help me through my ordeal and grant me better than it after'[17] except Allah helped him through his ordeal and gave him better than it after." She said: "So when Abu

17 اللَّهُمَّ أجرْنِي فِيْ مُصِيبَتِي وَاخْلُفْ لِي خَيْرًا مِنْهَا *Allahumma ajirnee fee musibatee wa ikhlafli khairan minha*

Salamah (her husband) died, I said what I was told to say by the Messenger of Allah and Allah granted me better than him…the Prophet of Allah." *(Muslim, Book of Prayers)*

Umm Salamah ﷺ was granted the best of creation, *Rasulullah* ﷺ, the beloved of Allah ﷻ, as an answer to her *du'a* and as a reward for her patience. Though we may not receive the likes of what Umm Salamah ﷺ was given, we can still, *insha'Allah*, reap the bounties of patience during pregnancy.

Hopefully, the promise of such rewards will lighten trying times for us. When we assess all the promises of Allah ﷻ to those who have patience we can understand the words of the Prophet ﷺ: "Nobody can be given a blessing better and greater than patience." (Bukhari, Book of *Zakat*) Those who are patient receive:

1. The companionship of Allah ﷻ:

…for Allah is with those who patiently persevere. (Surah Al-Anfal 8:46)

2. Salutations from angels from every gate of paradise:

And angels shall enter unto them from every gate (with the salutation): 'Peace unto you for that ye persevered in patience!' (Surah Ar-Ra'd 13:23-24)

3. A reward without measure:

Those who patiently persevere will truly receive a reward without measure! (Surah Az-Zumar 39:10)

We should therefore use pregnancy and its quirks as a means of gaining purification, mercy, blessings and guidance. This is the fortunate case of a believer, that in every affair, good and bad, we are given a door to His pleasure:

> Strange are the ways of a believer for there is good in every affair of his and this is not the case with anyone else except in the case of a believer for if he has an occasion to feel delight, he thanks (God), thus there is a good for him in it, and if he gets into trouble and shows resignation (and endures it patiently), there is a good for him in it. *(Muslim, Book Pertaining to Piety and Softening of Hearts)*

Thanking Allah

Pregnancy is the perfect time to begin truly thanking Allah ﷻ for all the things we have in life. So many of the comforts that we have been given can be taken for granted; everything from our stomachs not being volatile, our sense of smell not being repelled by raw meat, our digestive systems not usually working at a snail's pace, our normal body shape and the list goes on. There are so many blessings in life that we enjoy, day in and day out, which we are now able to recognise as blessings, because we no longer have them during pregnancy. This level of appreciation is one we should cultivate within ourselves, as gratitude for all that we have in life, because Allah ﷻ says:

> *And remember when your Lord made [His promise] known: If you are grateful [to Me], I shall most certainly give you more and more, but if you show ingratitude, truly My punishment is severe indeed.* (Surah Ibrahim 14:7)

We can never be grateful enough to Allah ﷻ because absolutely everything that we have is from Him, but we can certainly be *more* grateful to Him:

> *And He gives you of all that you ask for. But if you count the favours of Allah, never will you be able to number them. Verily, man is given up to injustice and ingratitude.* (Surah Ibrahim 14:34)

If we are dissatisfied with what Allah ﷻ has chosen to give us and what He has decreed for us then He warns us of a severe punishment. This is why we must develop true gratitude within ourselves. Here are some ways in which we can improve our levels of thankfulness to Allah ﷻ:

1. To actually try and count the blessings that Allah ﷻ has bestowed on us. When we are making *tasbeeh* after *salah*, we can think of a blessing from Allah ﷻ every time we say "*SubhanAllah*" (Glorified is Allah), "*Alhamdulillah*" (All praise is due to Allah), and "*Allahu akbar*" (Allah is the Greatest), instead of letting our minds wander. We can marvel at how amazing it is that our babies start out as bundles of cells and only nine months later are full-term babies!

2. Not to look to those who are more fortunate than us, but to look at those who are less fortunate:

> There are two traits which if found within an individual, Allah will write him down as 'the grateful' and 'the patient': the first is for a person to look at the one above him in matters pertaining to the *deen* and then to follow him, and the second is to look at the one below him in matters of the world, and to praise (and thank) Allah for having bestowed him with the favours he enjoys. *(Tirmidhi, Description of the Day of Judgement)*

We often find ourselves yearning for possessions and qualities that we see in others: an expensive nursery and travel system, a compact bump, a size ten figure after birth, and so on, which makes us dissatisfied with what we have been given. We forget that, *alhamdulillah*, Allah ﷻ has provided us with a roof over our heads, countless clothes and has made us able to bear children. There are many people in the world today that do not have these bounties. There are people who do not have water to drink, those who are starving, homeless, lonely or poverty stricken. There are those in hospital fighting diseases, those who are bed-ridden and those who are dying. There are women whom Allah ﷻ has made childless. Instead of appreciating all that Allah ﷻ has blessed us with, we always look to want more. Let us change this attitude to one of gratitude by always looking to those who are less fortunate than us.

We also need to re-adjust our focus and look to those who are above us in matters of the *deen*. There are those who make *tahajjud* a regular *salah*, those who have memorised the entire Qur'an, those who give generous sums in charity, those who are able to make sure they never lie or backbite, those who constantly seek Allah's ﷻ forgiveness and those with excellent character. Imagine what such people have to offer their children. If there is nobody around us that we see such qualities in then there are those who have beautiful secret deeds, hidden from people, which draw them close to Allah ﷻ. If we do not know many good Muslims then we do know that hundreds and thousands of great Muslims are living today and have come before us: scholars, teachers of the Qur'an, martyrs, Prophets and their companions. When we stand alongside all these people, with the beloved of Allah ﷺ, on the Day of Judgement, how will we compare?

3. To thank Allah ﷻ constantly with our tongues and say "*Alhamdulillah*", recognising that what we have is from Allah ﷻ, so that an appreciation for this enters our hearts. If we learn the translations of the daily *du'as* for waking up, eating etc., we see that they all express gratitude. We can make these *du'as,* whilst being conscious of their meanings, a part of everyday life. Once these *du'as* are ingrained in our lives our children will also inherit this gratitude, *insha'Allah*. Take for example the *du'a* for putting on clothes that we can say ourselves and whilst dressing our babies:

اَلْحَمْدُ لِلّٰهِ الَّذِي كَسَانِي هذَا (الثَّوب) وَرَزَقَنِيه
مِنْ غَيْرِ حَوْلٍ مِنِّي وَلاَ قُوَّةَ

"All praise is for Allah who has clothed me with this (garment) and provided it for me, with no power nor might from myself." *(Abu Dawud, Book of Clothing)*

Such *du'as* remove from us the feeling of self-sufficiency, inculcate within us gratitude, fulfil a *sunnah* and help us remember and mention Allah ﷻ throughout our day.

4. To always remember our humble origins and how Allah ﷻ protected us and made us what we are today:

> *And Allah has brought you forth from your mother's womb knowing nothing, but He gave you hearing and sight and intelligence and affections so that you might have cause to be grateful.* (Surah An-Nahl 17:78)

As we are witnessing this miracle of Allah ﷻ happen within us: the giving of life, hearing, sight, intelligence and emotion to a new human being, this method of achieving gratitude should be easier for pregnant women (and mothers) than anybody else. It is Allah ﷻ who has bestowed us with every faculty for learning from even before we enter this world. He has made us able to do all that we can and He has given us all that we achieve.

5. To be grateful to people. The Prophet ﷺ said:

> Those who do not thank people do not thank Allah. *(Abu Dawud, Book of General Behaviour)*

> ...and whoever does you a good deed, recompense it. If you are unable then make *du'a* for him until you are sure that you have compensated him. *(Abu Dawud, Book of General Behaviour)*

6. Last but not least, we need to ask Allah ﷻ to help us in showing gratitude to Him. A good *du'a* that we can make in our *salah* is one from the *sunnah*:

اللَّهُمَّ أَعِنِّي عَلَى ذِكْرِكَ وَشُكْرِكَ وَحُسْنِ عِبَادَتِكَ

> The Prophet ﷺ told Mu'âdh ﵁: "By Allah, I love you, so do not forget to say at the end of every *salah*, 'O Allah, help me to remember You and to give thanks to You and to worship You well.'" *(Abu Dawud, Book of Prayers)*

This *du'a* fits beautifully with the verse:

> *Remember Me - I will remember you, and be grateful to me and reject not faith.* (Surah Al-Baqarah 2:152)

Allah ﷻ tells us in this verse that if we remember Him, He will surely remember us and so the Prophet ﷺ told Mu'âdh ﵁ to ask Allah ﷻ for help in remembering Him. Allah ﷻ commands us to be grateful to Him and so the Prophet ﷺ taught Mu'âdh رضي الله عنه to ask for help in thanking Him. Allah ﷻ forbids us to reject faith and the Prophet ﷺ instructed Mu'âdh رضي الله عنه to ask for help in worshipping Him well. We too can benefit from this lovely *du'a* at the end of our *salah*.

We, as pregnant women, should also realise how Allah ﷻ has favoured us with the blessing of bearing a child and realise that this is a gift that He does not bestow upon everyone:

> *He gives to whom He wills females, and He gives to whom He wills males. Or He couples them as males and females, and he renders whom He wills childless. Indeed, He is Knowing and Capable.* (Surah Ash-Shura 42:49-50)

Some of us may have had to wait a long time before Allah ﷻ gave us children. The wife of Ibrahim عليه السلام, Sarah, was about seventy years old before Allah ﷻ gave them the glad tidings of their son, Ishaq عليه السلام. We have not had to wait that long, if at all, and so this is yet another mercy from Allah ﷻ. We are surrounded by His mercies yet we fail to see them, so let us begin noticing these bounties and thanking Allah ﷻ for them all.

Where is my Waistline?!

Not all women are delighted with the swelling of their stomachs (and thighs, and face… or varicose veins or stretch marks etc!). The flagrant physical changes in our bodies, together with our colourful hormone levels, can be far from pleasing for many of us. We worry about attending functions or having guests because we do not look 'presentable'. We pester our husbands with questions about how big our bum looks and if he still finds us attractive.

There are days when we feel we would really just like our bodies back, thank you and goodnight!

We have to accept that our bodies are not our own anymore but shared by a new and very demanding little being. All our lives we have our bodies completely to ourselves with our own concept of personal space. Pregnancy throws this right out of the window. We cannot even sleep or eat as we used to now that we are expecting. At times, particularly when we are tired, this can become frustrating or upsetting. Let us remind ourselves that it is Allah ﷻ who gave us our bodies and the comforts we enjoyed in our pre-pregnancy days and it is He who has granted us a tiny new being within us who is now sharing this gift. Allah ﷻ has made our unborn a guest, only here temporarily, so let us enjoy this time with our special guest, before we reach a day when we can no longer enjoy this bounty. The sensation of carrying a baby, nurturing them and protecting them inside is one that cannot be captured in words and this feeling is one that all mothers miss once their child is born. As with so many things in life, we do not realise what we have and the good in them, until it is gone. Being pregnant may not always be easy but it is a time to take pleasure in.

For many of us, one of the most difficult aspects of pregnancy is coping with getting big, or even HUGE. Due to the images of women that our society has imprinted in our minds as acceptable, we can find it difficult to reconcile this now inherent yet fabricated ideal with the inescapable reality of gaining weight in pregnancy. The baby is getting bigger day by day and so that means we must too! Gaining weight is not an option in pregnancy – it is a need. We have to remember that we are nurturing a brand new being and that women who eat poorly during pregnancy have smaller and less healthy babies. Just as we have to listen to our bodies when they say 'I'm tired' or 'I need more sleep' during pregnancy, we have to once again surrender, within limits, to getting big. Of course, this does not mean that we 'eat for two' and slouch around the house becoming couch potatoes! The Prophet ﷺ told us that the worst vessel we can fill is our stomachs[18] (i.e. do not eat too much) and he ﷺ sought protection from laziness.[19] We can eat sensibly and healthily, and keep active, particularly during the second trimester when we are feeling more ourselves and may be putting on weight more quickly.

Pregnancy and our changing shape is also an opportunity to assess the importance we place upon our outward selves, particularly in comparison to our inner selves. Which comes first? Looking good or feeling good? *Rasulallah* ﷺ told us which Allah ﷻ prefers us to get right and which He places importance on:

> Allah does not look upon your bodies and your outward appearance but He looks at your hearts. *(Muslim, The Book of Virtue, Good Manners and Joining of the Ties of Relationship)*

Therefore, should we not busy ourselves with perfecting our hearts and minds rather than dwelling on the inevitable growth of various body parts, all of which shall *insha'Allah* disappear again soon anyway? If Allah ﷻ, the One we are to please over and above anyone else, even our own selves, is not concerned about what size we are then why worry about it as much as we do? There are far greater things we should be focusing on. Here is a poem that many of us need to hear every now and then,

18 Tirmidhi, Book of Asceticism

19 The Prophet ﷺ used to say, "O Allah, I seek refuge with You from distress, grief, incapacity, laziness, miserliness, cowardice, the burden of debt and from being overpowered by men." (Bukhari, Book of Invocations)

اللَّهُمَّ إِنِّي أَعُوذُ بِكَ مِنَ الْهَمِّ وَالْحَزَنِ، وَالْعَجْزِ وَالْكَسَلِ، وَالْبُخْلِ وَالْجُبْنِ، وَضَلَعِ الدَّيْنِ، وَغَلَبَةِ الرِّجَالِ

when we scrutinise ourselves in the mirror, that can help reset the balance for us when we frown at our reflection:

The World is Mine

Today, upon a bus,
I saw a girl with golden hair
and wished I was as fair.
When suddenly she rose to leave,
I saw her hobble down the aisle.
She had one leg and wore a crutch.
But as she passed, a smile.
Ya Allah, forgive me when I whine.
I have two legs, the world is mine.

I stopped to buy some candy.
The lad who sold it had such charm.
I talked with him, he seemed so glad.
If I were late, it'd do no harm.
And as I left, he said to me,
"I thank you, you've been so kind.
It is nice to talk with folks like you.
You see," he said, "I'm blind."
Ya Allah, forgive me when I whine.
I have two eyes, the world is mine.

Later while walking down the street,
I saw a child with eyes of blue.
He stood and watched the others play.
He did not know what to do.
I stopped a moment and then I said,

"Why do you not join the others, dear?"
He looked ahead without a word.
And then I knew, he could not hear.
Ya Allah, forgive me when I whine.
I have two ears, the world is mine.

With feet to take me where I would go.
With eyes to see the sunset's glow.
With ears to hear what I would know.
Ya Allah, forgive me when I whine.
I have been blessed indeed, the world is mine.[20]

The next time we look in the mirror let us thank Allah ﷻ by saying:

الْحَمْدُ لِلّٰهِ اللَّهُمَّ كَمَا حَسَّنْتَ خَلْقِي فَحَسِّنْ خُلُقِي

> "All praises are due to Allah, O Allah, as you have given me a good physical form, so also favour me with good morals and manners." *(Mishkat, Book of Softness, Modesty and Good Character)*

'Awrah and Exposure of the Body

The number of people that see our bellies (and below) during pregnancy is incredible. There are the doctors and midwives we see very regularly, the ultrasonographer during ultrasound scans, and of course, the crew during labour and birth. As the focus of attention is our tummies and below, we need to be careful about who sees it and when! This is part of the '*awrah* that must remain covered before everyone, except our husbands, unless it is

20 Ahmed Khan (2002), Islamic Voice, Volume 15-09, No.189

medically required to be exposed. Yes, that means that getting our legs waxed because we can not reach them ourselves comfortably anymore isn't a valid reason for exposure! Being careful about uncovering our '*awrah* is an important requirement of a Muslim woman and not something to be taken lightly. The seriousness in covering the '*awrah* is seen in how it is described as a part of modesty, and how modesty is a tenet of faith:

> Every *deen* has an innate character. The character of Islam is modesty. *(Al-Muwatta, Book of Character)*

> Faith consists of more than sixty branches (i.e. parts). And *haya* (modesty) is a part of faith. *(Bukhari, Book of Belief)*

We are required by the law of Allah ﷻ to cover ourselves as outlined in the Qur'an:[21]

> *Say to the believing men that they should lower their gaze and guard their modesty: that will make for greater purity for them: and Allah is well acquainted with all that they do. And say to the believing women that they should lower their gaze and guard their modesty; that they should not display their beauty and ornaments except what (must ordinarily) appear thereof; that they should draw their veils over their bosoms and not display their beauty except to their husbands their fathers their husbands' fathers their sons their husbands' sons their brothers or their brothers' sons or their sisters' sons or their women or the slaves whom their right hands possess or male servants free of physical needs or small children who have no sense of the shame of sex; and that they should not strike their feet in order to draw attention to their hidden ornaments. And O you Believers! Turn you all together towards Allah that you may attain Bliss.*
> (Surah An-Nur 24:30-31)

21 For a fuller explanation of the rulings regarding covering, please see Dr. Jamal Badawi (2005), *The Muslim Woman's and Muslim Man's Dress According to the Qur'an and Sunnah*, Ta-Ha Publishers

This covering is not constrained to the presence of men only. We must also cover, although to a lesser extent, in front of women:

> A man should not look at the '*awrah* of another man nor a woman of another woman, nor should a man go under one cloth with another man, nor a woman with another woman. *(Muslim, Book of Menstruation)*

Often, during labour and birth, modesty and how much of the body is on show becomes a peripheral concern. Rather, this concern may not even surface at all. However, it is when later reflecting on the birthing experience that feelings of shame, guilt and regret often manifest themselves and they can be demoralising. We can avoid any negative post perception of the birth of our baby if we are firm on preserving our modesty, as far as we can, thus ensuring that having a baby is as special as can be. We can help achieve this with a little preparation and planning.

When dealing with the medical profession we can request female staff in advance. This is possible with the ultrasound scans, we can either ask our doctor or midwife to do this when applying for the scans, or phone the hospital ourselves. It is rarely a problem as most ultrasonographers will be women, but we can make sure. We can also request that our doctor and midwife are females if they are not already and request any *Muslimahs* that work on the team.

For labour, it is easy to state clearly in the birth plan that we would like to be attended to by females only, unless we are genuinely medically required to have male staff. We can be treated by men in limited cases such as when female staff with the appropriate and adequate skills are not available. If and when we need attention from male doctors only the necessary body parts should be uncovered and handled by the male doctor.[22] Make life easy for them and relieve some stress by making sure these requests are made beforehand. These requests will not sound strange to anybody as many pregnant women, be they Muslim or not, ask for female only staff.[23]

If we are able to receive care from the same midwife, or a few midwifes, throughout pregnancy, birth and postnatal period, we should do so. It is better that one woman, or a few women, see you rather than a whole band of medical staff.

When listening to the baby's heartbeat (after the first trimester when it becomes detectable) most midwives and doctors will be using sonic aids. These devices can be placed under loose fitting tops. A *kameez* (long, loose tunic) works very well as it has slits on both sides and is usually quite long in length. The same applies to monitoring the foetal heartbeat during labour when an electronic monitor wrapped around the abdomen is used. If a more old-fashioned instrument, called a pinnard stethoscope, is used where the doctor/midwife must place their ear near the stomach and on the instrument itself, a *kameez* will not help. The pinnard stethoscope is now rarely used and so this *insha'Allah* should not be a problem.

A further consideration is clothing worn to appointments and around medical staff. Ensure that sleeves can easily be rolled up for blood tests and for measuring blood pressure. Wear clothing which does not need to be removed in order to expose the required body parts and that can be pulled back down again quickly.

22 "If a woman has a wound in a part of the body that is impermissible for a male to look at it will be impermissible for her to receive treatment from a male doctor, rather a female should be instructed to treat her. If a female expert is not available, neither is there a female who can be instructed to treat her… then in such a case it would be permitted for a male doctor to treat her, provided there is a genuine need. It will be necessary for her to cover other than the affected area, and he must lower his gaze as much as possible." (al-Fatawa al-Hindiyya, 5/330)

23 E.g. Wright, C. M. (1989), Journal of the Royal College of General Practitioners, 33:101-104

For example, wear a separate top and trousers/skirt for breast or abdominal examinations. This will ensure that only the necessary parts are visible and for only the necessary length of time. We can keep exposure to a minimum, both in terms of how long we are exposed and how much is exposed in order to fulfil our obligations on modesty and save ourselves from discomfiture.

Some examinations, particularly in antenatal appointments, can be done over clothing. For example, if we wear a top made from a fairly thin fabric, the fundal height can be measured on our tummies over the top rather than us having to expose our bellies. In early pregnancy the fundal height is very low down, just above the pubic bone, and it continues to rise up towards our belly buttons by roughly a centimetre every week. This measure gives a guide to the progress in pregnancy and is achieved by pressing on the stomach to feel where the top of the uterus lies. As it is not a visible line that the midwife looks for, most will be happy to do this over light clothing as they are relying on their sense of touch, not sight.

Many women, particularly Muslim women, feel shy or embarrassed, if not humiliated, when being examined, even if it be by another female. Other women are able to bear the feelings of discomfort as they focus on how this is medically required for their health, and the health of their baby. Health professionals are increasingly aware of the differing cultural and religious needs of women. It is not new for them to come across women who keep their legs covered even when exposing far more intimate areas of the body, even during birth.[24]

A further note on '*awrah* concerns foetal imaging. Many of us may not realise that the internal organs, and therefore the uterus and its contents, including the baby, are also part of our

---

24 Schott, J. & Henley, A. (1996), *Culture, Religion and Childbearing in a Multiracial society - A handbook for professionals,* Oxford; Boston: Butterworth-Heinemann

'*awrah*. Due to this, together with exposure of our own bodies, the number of ultrasound scans we choose to have should also be given some thought. In uncomplicated pregnancies scans are not always necessary. If we do have to have a scan, and can take the photographs home with us, then they should only be shared with husbands as they are the only ones for whom our entire body is *halal* to view! Everybody else just has to wait to see the little one!

We should also note that not only do we have our own '*awrah* that we need to observe but we are also instructed by the Prophet ﷺ that a woman must not look at the '*awrah* of another woman. This would apply specifically to pregnancy with regards to antenatal sessions when explicit videos are often presented. We may choose to attend such classes and opt not to view the clips or photographs presented, or we can avoid the classes altogether. Alternatives to antenatal classes include finding someone who is willing to appropriately prepare us for labour and birth independently, or to study the birthing process ourselves. There is a wealth of literature available and so this task is entirely feasible. It can often prove more satisfying and serves as better preparation for us, and our families, than antenatal classes by allowing us to focus on issues that are relevant to our personal needs at our own pace.

The concern Muslim women have for their '*awrah* is one that the medical profession is often sensitive to and aware of. It is Muslim women themselves who are often uncomfortable with being prudent and surrender our modesty in an effort to not appear 'overly' modest. There is no such thing as being overly modest as modesty is an attribute that has greater value when observed to a greater degree. Just as a person cannot be too intelligent, one cannot be excessively modest. *Rasulallah* ﷺ said, "Modesty results in good alone and nothing else." (Muslim, Book of Faith). Rather, an extensive degree of modesty in a person is a quality to be admired, as was the modesty of the prophets and all those beloved to Allah ﷻ. Let us not succumb to our own lack of self-will and maintain our required levels of modesty during our pregnancy.

Stress in Pregnancy

Life is laden with worry and stress, as Allah ﷻ, says:

> *Verily, We have created man in toil.* (Surah Al-Balad 90:4)

During pregnancy, everyday stressors can become aggravated. Not only do we have our normal worries, to be handled by a not-so-normal body and mind, we also have a whole new set of worries that come with being pregnant! The first thing to reassure ourselves with is that it is normal to worry and to be stressed at times in life, particularly when pregnant. Maryam *alayhas salaam*, the mother of Isa عليه السلام, was under so much stress due to her pregnancy that she said:

> *Would that I had died before this, and had been forgotten and out of sight!* (Surah Maryam 19:23)

She was worried because she knew how people would think the worst of her when she came, unmarried, with her newborn.

The Prophets of Allah ﷻ and His righteous slaves, such as Maryam *alayhas salaam*, suffer the greatest amounts of stress in this world. Their suffering and anxiety supersedes ours by far.

> Sa'd رضي الله عنه asked the Prophet ﷺ: "O Messenger of Allah, which of the people suffers the most distress?" He said, "The Prophets, then those who come after them (in terms of status), then those who come after them. A man will be tested according to

> the strength of his faith. If his faith is strong, then the distress with which he is tried will be greater. If his faith is weak, he will be tested in accordance with the level of his faith. Distress will keep on befalling the slave until he walks on the face of the earth free from sin." *(Tirmidhi, Book of Asceticism)*

So, strangely enough, we can find comfort in calamity and times of stress as these may well befall us due to Allah's ﷻ love for us and can be a means of purification for us! This is one of the first ways in which we can begin stress relief; to know how fortunate we are as believers during our times of trial:

> Strange are the ways of a believer for there is good in every affair of his and this is not the case with anyone else except in the case of a believer, for if he has an occasion to feel delight, he thanks (Allah ﷻ), thus there is a good for him in it, and if he gets into trouble and shows resignation (and endures it patiently), there is a good for him in it. *(Muslim, Book Pertaining to Piety and Softening of Hearts)*

It is important to remember that everyday worries and anxiety will not damage your baby's health or development. Vivette Glover, professor of Perinatal Psychobiology at Imperial College, London, says: "It is also important to note that mood swings are common in pregnancy and that most mums-to-be will have times when they are worried."[25] *Alhamdulillah*, most women cope well with the physical demands on their bodies during pregnancy and with associated psychological changes.

Concerns arise for pregnant women who have persistent or

25 See Glover, V. & O'Connor, T. (2002), British Journal of Psychiatry, 180: 389-391 and related comments in a U.K. BBC press release titled, "Mother's anxiety affects baby's brain" 31/8/2001

chronic stress, particularly during the third trimester, or those who feel they are unable to cope with stress. Everybody knows that stress is bad for your health if it is maintained over a long-term. During pregnancy, stress may be harmful if it affects your behaviour. For example, women change eating habits under stress, such as eating too little or not choosing nutritious foods, and we all know that we should be eating well and healthily during pregnancy.

Also remember that because stress has a distinct biochemical pattern where particular hormones are released, our baby not only knows that we are stressed, but also shares the chemicals we produce in response to stress. The effects of this were seen in an analysis of over 2000 babies where it was found that the risk of low birth weight was significantly related to perceived stress during pregnancy.[26] Studies also suggest that high levels of stress may contribute to other pregnancy complications such as pre-eclampsia.[27]

There are strategies we can all employ to alleviate stress and its effects. Interventions when pregnant have been shown to help improve pregnancy outcomes and so even if we cannot take stress out of our lives, we can remove stress as a worry-factor in pregnancy. There are steps we can all employ at home to help do this. The following are methods of combating stress:

1. *Dhikr*

The remembrance of Allah ﷻ calms the soul and relieves stress and worry, Allah ﷻ says:

> *Verily, in the remembrance of Allah do hearts find rest.* (Surah Al-Ra'd 13:28)

26 Sable, M. R. & Wilkinson, D.S. (2000), Family Planning Perspectives, 32(6):288-294

27 Hobel, C. J. et al. (1999), American Journal of Obstetrics and Gynecology, 180(1):S257–S263

Dhikr is the perfect remedy for pregnant women with rampaging hormones who cannot remember the last time they had a restful night's sleep. A heart at peace is a bliss that few know and all desire. We can achieve this, recharge and refocus, by remembering Allah ﷻ. When we worry about which type of pushchair we should splash out on, or are traumatised by the thought of birth, we can find comfort in remembering Allah ﷻ. We can read Qur'an,[28] stand up in prayer, or simply mention His name to remind ourselves that it is Allah ﷻ who plans and is the best of planners, it is He who provides for each and every one of us, even the hungry bird that leaves its nest every morning, not knowing where it will find its food. It is Allah ﷻ who has power over all things and nothing happens except by His leave, whether we worry about it or not. So let us remember Allah ﷻ and put our trust in Him and grant our hearts peace!

2. *Du'a*

Allah ﷻ knows even the falling of every leaf (Surah Al-An'am 6:59). Therefore, when you may feel that nobody understands or there is nobody you can talk to, know that Allah ﷻ is All-Seeing and All-Hearing, Most Kind and Most Merciful, the Loving and the Generous, and He is always there, always listening:

> *And when My slaves ask you concerning Me, then (answer them), I am indeed near. I respond to the invocations of the supplicant when he calls on Me.* (Surah Al-Baqarah 2:186)

28 There is particular benefit in reciting Chapter 36, Ya-Seen, after *Fajr*. "Whosoever recites Surah Ya-Seen in the early part of the day, his needs will be fulfilled." (Darimi, Virtues of Qur'an)

There are specific *du'as* that we can make to alleviate stress, such as:

اللَّهُمَّ إِنِّي أَعُوذُ بِكَ مِنَ الْهَمِّ وَالْحَزَنِ، وَالْعَجْزِ وَالْكَسَلِ، وَالْبُخْلِ وَالْجُبْنِ، وَضَلَعِ الدَّيْنِ، وَغَلَبَةِ الرِّجَالِ

"O Allah, I seek refuge with You from distress, grief, incapacity, laziness, miserliness, cowardice, the burden of debt and from being overpowered by men." *(Bukhari, Book of Invocations)*

اللَّهُمَّ إِنِّي عَبْدُكَ وَابْنُ عَبْدِكَ وَابْنُ أَمَتِكَ نَاصِيَتِي بِيَدِكَ مَاضٍ فِيَّ حُكْمُكَ عَدْلٌ فِيَّ قَضَاؤُكَ أَسْأَلُكَ بِكُلِّ اسْمٍ هُوَ لَكَ سَمَّيْتَ بِهِ نَفْسَكَ أَوْ عَلَّمْتَهُ أَحَدًا مِنْ خَلْقِكَ أَوْ أَنْزَلْتَهُ فِي كِتَابِكَ أَوِ اسْتَأْثَرْتَ بِهِ فِي عِلْمِ الْغَيْبِ عِنْدَكَ أَنْ تَجْعَلَ الْقُرْآنَ رَبِيعَ قَلْبِي وَ نُورَ صَدْرِي وَجَلاَءَ حُزْنِي وَذَهَابَ هَمِّي

"There is no-one who is afflicted by distress and grief, and says: 'O Allah, I am Your slave, son of Your slave, son of Your maidservant; my forelock is in Your hand, Your command over me is forever executed and Your decree over me is just. I ask You by every name belonging to You which You have named Yourself with, or revealed in Your Book, or You taught to any of Your creation, or You have preserved in the knowledge of the Unseen with You, that You make the Qur'an the life of my heart and the light of my breast, and a departure for my sorrow and a release for my anxiety.'" *(Ahmad 3704)*

3. Be Grateful

Appreciating the blessings Allah has showered us with lifts the soul:

> If anyone of you looked at a person who was made superior to him in property and (in good) appearance, then he should also look at the one who is inferior to him, and to whom he has been made superior. *(Bukhari, Book to make the Heart Tender)*

4. Concern for the Hereafter

> Whoever has this world as his main concern, Allah will cause him to feel constant fear of poverty; he will be distracted and unfocused, and he will have nothing of this world except what was already predestined for him. Whoever has the Hereafter as his main concern, Allah will fill his heart with a feeling of richness and independence; he will be focused and feel content, and this world will come to him in spite of it. *(Ibn Majah, Book of Asceticism)*

5. Trust in Allah ﷻ

> *And whosoever puts his trust in Allah, then He will suffice him.* (Surah At-Talaq 65:3)

> The Messenger of Allah ﷺ said: "The strong believer is better and more beloved to Allah than the weak believer, and both are good. Pay attention to that which could benefit you, seek the help of Allah and do not feel incapacitated. If anything befalls you, do not say, 'If only I had done such-and-such, such a thing would have happened.' Say instead, 'It is the decree of Allah, and what He wills, He does,' for saying 'if only…' opens the way for *Shaytan*." *(Muslim, Book of Destiny)*

Rather than looking back and regretting or despairing, think ahead and know that with hardship there is ease as Allah ﷻ says:

So verily, with hardship, there is relief, verily, with hardship, there is relief. (Surah As-Sharh 94:5-6)

Remember that feeling low or stressed during pregnancy is rather normal and should not become a worry in itself. However, stress can be exacerbated by spending time thinking about situations that are stressful, not making time to relax and by taking on too much. There are simple steps we can take to combat these. The strategies outlined in the section below are practical tips we can all employ in order to tackle stress aggravators. We can also emphasise activities that take our attention from stress, such as spending time with friends and with Qur'an, reading and exercising. Whilst maintaining a healthy balance of expressing our thoughts and concerns, we need to ensure that we are not thinking and talking excessively about what is distressing us, particularly if it involves negative thoughts about ourselves. Often, stress can be managed by changing how we think and assess our daily lives. For a Muslim, the best thing we can train our minds with is by combining the advice above: relying on Allah ﷻ and trusting in Him, and by making *du'a* for all that is best for our faith, our lives and most importantly, our Hereafter.

اللَّهُمَّ رَحْمَتَكَ أَرْجُو فَلا تَكِلْنِي إِلى نَفْسِي طَرْفَةَ عَيْنٍ،
وَأَصْلِحْ لِي شَأْنِي كُلَّهُ لاَ إِلَهَ إِلاَّ أَنْتَ

"O Allah, for Your mercy I hope, so do not leave me in charge of my affairs even for the blink of an eye; rectify all my affairs. There is no god except You." *(Abu Dawud, Book of Sleep)*

Depression during Pregnancy

"Beautifully joyful, glowing, rosy cheeks with a smile on her face" is the pretty picture of a pregnant women. But, as we know, it is a myth that pregnant women are in constant bliss. We have our good and bad days, maybe even more bad days than good, so much so that pregnancy does not make us immune to depression. Current statistics suggest that depression can affect ten to sixteen percent of women during pregnancy.[29] Many women feel confused by how they are feeling because pregnancy is "supposed" to be a time when you are happy. In fact, the symptoms of depression can be misdiagnosed or ignored in pregnant women because they are so similar to the symptoms of pregnancy. So being pregnant is not very different to being depressed at times!

Pregnancy can be a trying time. There can be times when we feel low. Some of us may also have to manage clinical depression for part, or all, of our pregnancy. Finding treatment for depression is equally as important as treating any other health concerns whilst pregnant. Our mental health is an *amanah* (trust) in the same way as our physical health and we should maintain both, the best we can. When feeling ill people do not think twice about seeking medical aid or rest – our mental health deserves the same, if not more attention.

Despite depression being common, most people know very little about it and do even less about it. There are steps we can take at home to manage depression and we can see our doctor. After seeking medical advice we do not necessarily have to resort to drug treatment, though this is available and often recommended for severe depression. There is also therapy. This does not mean the stereotypical lying on a couch and talking about childhood

29 Kahn, D. A., Moline, L. M., Ross, R. W., Cohen, L. S., Altshuler, L. L. (2001), *Major Depression during Conception and Pregnancy: A Guide for Patients and Families.*

experiences to a neo-Freudian character. New therapy that is particularly effective for depression tackles negative thinking patterns and behaviour.[30] This can be done from a self-help book or a computer programme. The bottom line is that there is something that can be done about depression: we can seek help.

For those of us feeling the blues (without necessarily being depressed) there are things we can try at home to help:

1. Get a helping hand

There are often times when we feel tired, even if we are not depressed. It just comes with being pregnant. Ask for help with the cooking and cleaning or any other daily tasks. People are particularly considerate, generous and helpful during pregnancy so we do not have to feel that we must do it all alone. People are happy to help. We need to learn to set new goals and priorities based on how we feel each day or week, leaving tasks that we may have normally been sure to have done, but are not necessary, and we can do with leaving.

2. Exercise

If we do not already do any regular exercise then we need to discuss any big changes with our doctor first. Try going for a walk, even if it is just ten minutes to begin with. Exercise is one of the body's natural ways of dealing with the hormone cortisol that is involved in depression (and stress). Our bodies also release hormones during and after exercise that leave us feeling good and aid sleep. Try planning regular, safe exercise into every day,

---

30 This includes Cognitive Behavioural Therapy (CBT), which focuses on negative thoughts and teaches different ways of thinking and behaving in order to combat depression. There is also Interpersonal Therapy (IPT), which targets methods of effective communication with others. It must be stressed that therapy deals with our mental makeup and should ideally be sought from practicing Muslim therapists. For a Muslim, faith is the driving force in how we view and perceive the world and only those who share this can appreciate this fact.

or for half the days of the week. Stationary cycling or pilates at home might be the option as these can be done in the privacy of our own homes and places no pressure on the back or joints. We can also try going for walks or swimming. There are usually women-only slots and sessions for pregnant women. We can ask beforehand if these times have female lifeguards only and if there are no men attending the security cameras.

3. Get enough sleep

We need enough sleep to have a healthy pregnancy and also to stop symptoms of depression getting worse. Many pregnant women do experience problems sleeping for various reasons which we need to try and combat. Relax before going to bed, perhaps try having a warm bath and reading some Qur'an, such as reciting Surah Al-Mulk (67) or Surah As-Sajdah (32)[31] before sleeping to take our mind off the worries of the world. Trying to regulate bedtimes and when we begin our day can also aid sleep.

4. Make some "Me time"

We all need some time to ourselves together with time when we can do what we enjoy. When feeling run down or low we might not like doing things we normally enjoy. Try doing these things when feeling better, even if starting them is not always what we feel like doing. In addition to time alone, we need to spend time with others even if we feel like we are not great company.

---

31 The Prophet ﷺ never used to sleep until he had recited Surah Al-Mulk and Surah As-Sajdah. (Tirmidhi, Virtues of Qur'an)

Thinking of Death with the Start of Life

Strangely enough, the start of a new life inside us can make us more conscious of death. With the risk of miscarriage in the first trimester being so significant (the percentage being perhaps as high as thirty percent in first pregnancies) pregnant women often contemplate the cycle of life and death. Many women come to understand the fragility of life and just how little control we have over it. We neither choose when to start life nor when to end it.

This realisation of the power and ultimate control of Allah ﷻ coupled with our sensitivity to the terminal nature of life, can do wonders for our *'ibadah* and *iman*. Pregnancy is a time during which the focus is very much on ourselves and on the forthcoming weeks and months. At times, it can be difficult to think beyond our due dates and to focus on things that are not pregnancy related.

As *Muslimahs,* we know that time in the womb is only a fraction of a much longer journey of the soul. Maintaining this long view and highlighting its importance aids us in forming firm foundations for strengthening our own souls, in order to be the best we can be for our children to come, *insha'Allah.*

The life in the womb is one of protection and comfort, encased in our mothers, who love us even before they meet us. However, the seven star service of the womb must end. When Allah ﷻ wills, the baby leaves the precious uterus to enter a collage of sights and sounds, out on its own.

The contrast between the world in the womb and our world is unimaginable. The greatest of comforts for our babies (or rather their lifeline), to be immersed in the amniotic fluid of the womb, supported by the placenta, listening to the mothers heartbeat, would suffocate us. For us, having no air to breathe, being in a confined space with restricted movement, alone with only muffled voices for company would be tormenting.

At the time of birth, our babies await a radical change in environment as they join our world. Faced with the need to breathe, no longer cushioned in our uterus, flooded with every new sight, and being held for the first time in a world never felt before is an experience we cannot appreciate. Worryingly, a similar transition, is something we will all face again, at the end of our time in this world. Thus, the beginning of life is a reminder of the end of life.

It may seem depressing to discuss death and the Hereafter, and it might seem like the last thing we want to think about when pregnant, but the Prophet ﷺ has advised us to do exactly this; to remember death:

> Keep much in remembrance death which is the cutter-off of pleasure, for a day does not come to the grave without its saying, "I am the house of exile, I am the house of solitude, I am the house of dust, I am the house of worms." *(Tirmidhi, Book of Characteristics of the Day of Judgement)*

The Messenger of Allah ﷺ has told us that remembering death is actually good for us. As pregnant women, we should soak up all that is good for us. We look after our physical selves better than usual when carrying a baby and this extra care and pampering should also be applied to our hearts and souls. *Rasulallah* ﷺ has told us that the way to pamper or polish our hearts is to remember death:

> "These hearts become rusty just as iron does when water affects it." On being asked what could clear them he replied, "A great amount of remembrance of death and recitation of the Qur'an." *(Bayhaqi 2/1352, No. 2014)*

This polishing of our hearts is an ideal way to prepare ourselves for our journey of motherhood. It is the foundation for improving oneself and striving to continually grow and achieve as believers. Many of us may feel that we have a dip in our *iman* during the difficult stages of pregnancy, especially when we feel unwell and cannot do as much as we would like to in terms of '*ibadah. Insha'Allah*, the remembrance of death and its contemplation is one way in which we can revive our *iman*.

Breastfeeding

During pregnancy we need to think about how we will feed our newborn baby. Ninety-four percent of pregnant women agree that breast milk is better for their babies but only seventy-six percent of these women intend breastfeeding.[32] Why is this the case when Allah ﷻ has made breast milk a unique, specially designed food and drink for babies? So perfect is breast milk that Allah ﷻ has enjoined it on women nursing their children and has made breastfeeding a right of the newborn.

Today, however, we are presented with breastfeeding as a choice, not an obligation to Allah ﷻ. Psychological perspectives on pregnancy and childbirth use the term "decision-making" when discussing breastfeeding whilst presenting various models for the thought processes and factors involved in women's choices about how to feed their new baby. Some even refer to "women-centred" and "child-centred" reasons for breastfeeding, such as convenience and infant health benefits respectively. For us, breastfeeding is a duty. Allah ﷻ Himself mentions breastfeeding in the Qur'an, for example:

32 Hawthorne, K. (1994), Modern Midwife, March: 24-28

The mothers shall give suck to their offspring for two whole years if the father desires to complete the term. (Surah Al-Baqarah 2:233)[33]

Breast milk, being a gift from Allah ﷻ, is miraculous. The literature on the benefits of breast milk for both mums and babies is vast. Here is just one example: The protein content of breast milk is indirectly proportional to the maturity of the newborn baby.[34] In other words, the smaller the baby, the higher the protein content of the mother's milk. In fact, the protein content (which is what is important for the baby) in our milk is not constant and varies from day to day and even at different times during the same day, to suit the exact needs of the baby.

Despite these unparalleled benefits of breastfeeding, many pregnant women decide against it, or only consider it as a possibility. This is probably due to a combination of factors such as bottle-feeding having been portrayed as the modern, easy option and breastfeeding being "difficult". This stereotype is not true – it's not like comparing a vacuum cleaner to a broom! Breasts were designed by Allah, the Creator and Originator, for feeding babies; bottles and formula milk are manufactured by short-sighted man.

The majority of women make decisions on how to feed their baby much in advance of giving birth and those who have made firm decisions in pregnancy have been found not to change their minds once their baby is born.[35] It is therefore well worth reading up on the various benefits of breastfeeding in order to solidify our intentions to feed our babies the way in which Allah ﷻ has prescribed, and to make abundant *du'a* whilst pregnant for

---

33 Two lunar years is the maximal period of breastfeeding.

34 Atkinson, J. A, Bryan, H. & Anderson, H. (1981), Journal of Pediatrics, 99:617

35 Oxby, H. (1994), Health visitor, 67(5):161

Allah ﷻ to make breastfeeding easy for us and our baby, and for us to be able to breastfeed for as long as is best for us both.

Many women can encounter problems when breastfeeding, particularly in the first few days and weeks with the baby, as both mum and baby need to learn how to feed. There is a lot of help available for women that intend to/are breastfeeding. However, a few women may need to abandon their ideals of breastfeeding. In some cases, there is no choice but to bottle-feed, be it temporarily, and so it is worth doing some cursory preparation and reading up on bottle-feeding too, just in case, by the will of Allah ﷻ, our intention to breastfeed does not become a reality. *Insha'Allah* for those of us this may apply to, we receive the reward of breastfeeding, plus the reward for bottle-feeding our babies!

Let us also note that women can also reap the benefits of breastfeeding when pregnant, if we are still breastfeeding a previous child. We can continue to breastfeed our babies when pregnant without fearing anything for our unborn. The Messenger of Allah ﷺ said:

> I considered prohibiting breastfeeding whilst pregnant, but I observed the Byzantines and Persians that they breastfeed their children during pregnancy and their children are not harmed. *(Muslim, Book of Marriage)*

Husbands of Pregnant Women

> *And among His Signs is this, that He created for you mates from among yourselves, that you may dwell in tranquillity with them, and He has put love and mercy between your (hearts): verily in that are Signs for those who reflect.* (Surah Ar-Rum 30:21)

After having discussed our own perspectives on pregnancy let us not forget the daddies of our babies. Our dear husbands are often the only ones who can fully participate in the excitement of our pregnancy and in the attachment we have to our babies. Husbands form part of the social support network that we all need before, during and after pregnancy. They are there for us physically and emotionally. Expecting their child, we take on a new beauty and concern in their hearts. *Insha'Allah*, this is a time for us to be treated extra-specially by our husbands and a time when many men strive to truly fulfil the *sunnah* of *Rasulallah* ﷺ:

> The most perfect Muslim in the matter of faith is one who has excellent behaviour; and the best among you are those who behave best towards their wives. *(Tirmidhi, Book of Breastfeeding)*

As pregnant women, society often expects us to receive this pampering from our husbands (and maybe everyone else too!). It is even normal for women who are having healthy, very smoothly running pregnancies to be excused from preparing a simple salad. Often during pregnancy the concept that we, as wives, are also to be there for our husbands in an equally supportive manner can also be eroded, or even forgotten. On our part, as Muslim women, it can help to re-assess by remembering that Allah سبحانه وتعالى describes the relationship between man and wife as:

> *They are your garments and you are their garments.* (Surah Al-Baqarah 2:187)

This role of protection, adornment and support Allah ﷻ describes applies equally to both partners at all times. There is not an excused period during pregnancy when only dear husband is a garment for us and we are on holiday from our role of wife. For example, during pregnancy we may have the excuse to stay in our pyjamas until lunchtime because we do not feel well in the morning or because we have not slept well at night (or we may be excusing ourselves until the doorbell rings!), but when we are feeling better we should make the effort to look good for our husbands:

> Shall I tell you the best a man can treasure? It is a good wife. If he looks at her, she gives him pleasure; if he orders her, she obeys; and if he is away from her, she remains faithful to him. *(Abu Dawud, Book of Zakat)*

We fit this description much more closely when we make the effort to look nice for our husbands! We should ask ourselves: do I look better for my midwife or my husband? Did I last do my hair removal before that appointment or before the weekend we had time at home together? Who do I wear ironed clothes for? When we make an effort at home we will also *insha'Allah* find that we feel better and more attractive ourselves which can be a pleasant change for everyone!

Many husbands are often extremely accommodating to our changing physical and emotional needs; they give us our space when we need it and draw closer when we need them. They are known to go out at 2am to buy burgers or sweets to fulfil our cravings. They also have to exercise much self-restraint and control when it comes to intimacy. Understanding husbands will think not to approach us when we are tired, or feeling sick or are having trouble sleeping and so on. In return we should understand that our pregnancy is actually a big change for our husbands too.

Our husbands need to adjust to our varying emotional states, our ever-changing bodies and accustom themselves to the fact that there is a baby growing inside our bellies! As expectant mothers, we may take these adjustments in our stride. We come to terms with being pregnant much more quickly than our husbands do, as we are inseparable from this baby, every minute of our lives. We find our erratic mood swings far more forgivable than others will find them and it may irritate or upset us when our husbands do not sympathise with our feelings. It is a good reminder for us primarily, and for others, that pregnant women can have highly turbulent emotions. It is not the world that is at fault, it is our hormones in extreme overdrive. It is better to train ourselves to cope well with this rather than spite those around us. By taking time out or away, by rest, relaxation, and safe exercise, we can manage the consequences of our rampant hormone levels.

Though our husbands are enthusiastic about our pregnancy it does not permeate them in the same way as it does us, as mothers-to-be *insha'Allah*. We consider everything in the light of being pregnant and this may not always be the case with our husbands. This can be particularly true when it comes to intimacy.

We may unduly worry about harm to the baby, be tired or irritable, or just want to snuggle under the covers and have a good night's sleep. We might want to stay up and paint the nursery or talk about whether we should buy a cot or a cot bed. All these things just seem a lot less pertinent to our dear husband who would just like some time with his wife! During such times we can remember the following two sayings of the Prophet ﷺ:

> If a husband calls his wife to his bed (i.e. to have sexual relations) and she refuses and causes him to sleep in anger, the angels will curse her till morning. *(Bukhari, Book of Beginning of Creation)*

> Of the three people whose prayer does not pass beyond their ears is the woman who spends the night in a state in which her husband is annoyed with her. *(Ibn Hibban, Book of Drinks)*

Sure, if we are exhausted or unwell then *insha'Allah* our husbands understand and accommodate our needs. We should return this sensitivity and consideration and make sure that when we are feeling well that we fulfil his rights, both sexually and in terms of wider intimacy and understanding. During pregnancy our husbands' understanding for us can become too much of a norm and we need to recognise when we are simply taking advantage of their sympathetic attitude, and realise when we should be attentive to their needs too. This emphasis on mutual understanding will provide the best of foundations for good support during pregnancy and for life as new parents.

A further consideration is our heightened emotional states when pregnant. Unfortunately, it is dearest husband who is usually on the receiving end of bouts of anger and negativity. Many men will tell you it is tough being married to a pregnant woman and nine months is a long time to bear it all! There will be times when he will not be able to help us as much as we may need or like or will "fall short" in some other respect. It is important to remember that just as we are far from perfect and make mistakes, they cannot read our minds and they too are just as human as we are!

We should keep people's feelings in perspective, particularly those who are closest to us. Our husbands can often end up thinking, "You wanted to be pregnant, and now you are you're complaining all the time!" We need to focus more on their good deeds and the times that they have been generous, rather than home-in on the not-so-nice aspects. We should strive in always giving them the benefit of the doubt, finding excuses for them, thinking the best in them and overlooking their flaws:

> Hamdun al-Qassar said, "If a friend among your friends errs, make seventy excuses for them. If your hearts are unable to do this, then know that the shortcoming is in your own selves." *(Bayhaqi, Branches of Belief)*

This is particularly important when it comes to family. Often we treat our friends and acquaintances, even complete strangers, with great kindness, are very polite and on our best behaviour, but when it comes to those nearest and dearest to us, we are not always as pleasant and considerate. Having a baby, pregnancy included, puts a strain on even the best of marriages. The relationship between couples has been known in the psychological fields to be a classic indicator of both physical and mental health. Sadly, as an indicator of the increased pressures on couples during pregnancy, we know that domestic violence often starts, or worsens, during pregnancy.[36] This is the opposite of what should be happening to a pregnant woman.

These startling statistics also highlight how not all men have the patience and understanding that many women enjoy from their husbands. Though lots of women continue to work, be it part- or full-time, look after older children, or

---

36 Mezey, G. C., Domestic violence in pregnancy, cited in Bewley, S. et al. (1997), *Violence Against Women,* London, RCOG.

other members of the family whilst pregnant, there can be times when we need a break. We may not always be able to cook and clean as usual due to the added strain of pregnancy. Some women may be unable to fulfil certain responsibilities, or chores, and some may be unable to travel. Husbands should be accommodating, try to take on more tasks around the home, adopt a greater share in responsibilities and excuse us when we are not always able to do as much as we would normally. They should particularly be understanding when it comes to dealing with problems and be acutely aware that what they say and do is going to be received by a very emotional pregnant woman carrying his developing, unborn baby. It is not always easy growing a brand new human being!

It is important to work together in being amongst the best of wives and amongst the best of husbands, even during pregnancy, if not especially at this time. Therefore let us pray that our pregnancies are enjoyable for ourselves and for our husbands.

II.
Your Baby

Tiny fingers and tiny toes. A little button nose. Will it be like mine or like his? We imagine who our baby will look like. We picture ourselves holding them in our arms the day they are born. We rub our tummies with affection and speak to this invisible being we already love. We bear sickness and pain for this new life beginning inside us, because it is our baby.

This devotion we have to our unborn children is a bond that only grows stronger and deeper over time. Our children always teach us valuable lessons about ourselves and the learning begins during pregnancy. The love we have for our unborn baby can teach us something about *Rasulallah* ﷺ, his love for us and our love for him. As expectant mothers we have a glimpse of the deep concern he ﷺ had for us, his followers, even those he had never met. Our attachment to our baby also beautifully demonstrates how we can love the Messenger of Allah ﷺ despite never having seen his face.

This love for the baby we are carrying can manifest itself as a fear and concern for the well-being of our unborn. We sincerely pray that they are healthy, that they are free from defects and disease. We also beg Allah ﷻ for their mental and spiritual condition, praying that they are happy and righteous and that He makes them a source of joy and blessing for us.

We begin to lay the foundations of their world, prepare for them being a part of our families and we strive to do all that is best for the baby. Our pregnancy becomes a concerted effort in providing the best start in life, even before our baby takes its first breath.

I Can Hear You!

The elastic on our trousers seems more and more uncomfortable and yet this makes us smile gleefully. As our bump becomes increasingly noticeable, the attachment to our unborn intensifies. When we realise that this unborn baby can hear everything going on in the world around them, this bond takes on a newfound strength that words cannot capture. We find ourselves chatting to our tummy, singing to it and sharing our day with it. Knowing that our baby can hear us introduces them into our lives and makes them ever more a part of our world.

It is during the second trimester that our baby can hear us. Already sharing our bodies, our air and our food, they now also share all that we hear. Our babies already have the beginnings of their ears in the very first month of our pregnancy. Even before their ears are complete, they can hear and respond to sound.[37] Their sense of hearing begins around the eighth week of pregnancy and is complete by the twentieth week after conception.[38] Our baby is actively listening by the twenty-fourth week and can hear us potter around the kitchen, opening the fridge, chatting to our husbands. By eight months, sound sensation is fully activated and our baby is listening, just like us.

There is enough to ponder on with the development of the ear and hearing but also quite exciting is the fact that babies have a special focus on the mother's voice. Our voice undergoes very little distortion in the womb whereas everybody else's voices come across more muffled. "They get excited when they hear their mother's voice; it is something that they recognize and are

37 Shahidullah, S. & Hepper, P. (1992), International Journal of Prenatal and Perinatal Studies, 4 (3 and 4):235-240

38 Pujol, R., Lavigne-Rebillard, M. & Uziel, A. (1991), Acta Otolaryngologica, (482):7-12

aroused by," says Barbara Kisilevsky, of Queens University in Ontario, Canada.[39]

Exactly what effects the mother's voice has on the baby is not clear-cut but what we can be sure of is that they can hear us. Not only this, but babies can actually remember what they heard in the womb after they are born. They know our voice whilst we are carrying them and they know that this is the same beloved voice once they are born.

An example of this wonderful ability in newborns is seen in a study with two to four day old babies, whose mothers regularly heard the TV theme tune for the soap opera, "Neighbours", whilst pregnant. The newborns became alert, stopped moving and their heart rate fell when they heard the tune, indicating its familiarity.[40] They had not heard the tune after the birth and so the babies must have learned it prenatally, and remembered it two to four days after being born. So not only are they listening, they are listening and learning. This type of learning seems to take place after thirty weeks of gestation[41] - that bump in the final trimester is very alert!

As well as learning about the sounds that our baby hears, our unborn is also affected by these sounds, both emotionally and behaviourally. They can be calmed and soothed, or frightened and agitated, depending on what they hear.[42] In addition to sounds impinging on their own emotional states, our unborn can even associate sounds with specific emotional states.

---

39 See Kisilevsky, B. S., Hains, S. M. J., Lee, K., Xie, X., Huang, H., Ye, H. H., Zhang, K. & Wang, Z. (2003), Psychological Science 14:220-225 and Kirchheimer, S. (2003), in WebMD Medical News, 14/5/2003

40 Hepper, P. G. (1988), Lancet, 1347-8

41 Hepper, P. G. (1996), Acta Paediatrica (Stockholm), S416:16-20

42 Polverini-Rey, R. A. (1992), Dissertation Abstracts # 9233740

A particular way in which an unborn's emotions may be affected is by the mother's own emotions. The enzymes we produce when we undergo an emotion can cross over into the placenta and reach the baby. Our baby can therefore experience the same emotions as we do, at least on a biochemical level. Therefore, the things we find relaxing are also likely to calm and soothe our baby.

Based on these findings, we can try coupling a sound stimulus, such as talking softly, with feeling calm in order to use this as a comforter for our baby once they are born. For example, we can sit down in a quiet room that is not too brightly lit, breathe slowly and deeply and then recite a few of our favourite verses of the Qur'an. If our baby is responsive to having our tummy rubbed then we can also slowly massage or pat our stomach whilst reciting. If we try doing this regularly, especially once we are thirty weeks pregnant, we can then *insha'Allah* use the same verses to soothe our baby once born.

It is worth remembering that immediately after the birth we will not be able to recite Qur'an ourselves due to postnatal bleeding. All schools of jurisprudence are of the opinion that a woman must not recite Qur'an in the postnatal period, or during menstruation. However, we can make *du'a*, or send *salaam* to the Prophet ﷺ, or do *dhikr*. The logic behind using a familiar sound to soothe the baby is based on the premise that whatever reminds them of their cosy time in the womb will comfort them. This is also why swaddling a baby and having them close to the chest calms them - because they were tightly bundled in the womb, listening to the beating of our hearts.

The Remembrance of Allah ﷻ

Our unborn children can hear what we say, they listen to what we listen to and they share our emotions. Most importantly, they learn from all this. Whether we intend it or not, this learning forms the building blocks of their development and shapes the beginnings of their minds. As mothers praying for the best for our babies we can utilise this learning and actively teach them, in the best way possible, even during our pregnancy. It is from this earliest stage in life, enveloped in the womb, when our baby is already attentive, listening and learning that we can give them the best start in life, with the finest thing in life:

> *And remembrance of Allah is the greatest thing (in life) without doubt.* (Surah Al-Ankabut 29:45)

This is the remembrance of Allah ﷻ, the One who is the Giver of life to every soul, no matter how new.[43] The Qur'an, as well as expressions praising and glorifying Allah ﷻ, such as "*SubhanAllah*" (Glorified is Allah), "*Alhamdulillah*" (All praise is due to Allah), and "*Allahu akbar*" (Allah is the Greatest), whether they are said audibly or silently to oneself are *dhikr*, or the remembrance of Allah ﷻ.

When we remember Allah ﷻ we are given the beautiful gift of Allah ﷻ remembering us:

> *Remember Me, I shall remember you…* (Surah Al-Baqarah 2:152)

Imagine your most beloved mentioning you, as you think of Him. As the carriers of fragile souls we are in constant need of this; of Ar-Rahman remembering us. We need Allah's ﷻ protection,

43 "The likeness of the one who remembers his Lord and the one who does not remember Him is like that of a living to a dead person." (Bukhari, Book of Invocations)

mercy and blessings in extra doses, both for ourselves and for the tiny baby we are nurturing. We ask Allah ﷻ for our pregnancy to go well, for our babies to grow and develop, and to get us through labour and birth. We beg Allah ﷻ to show us mercy during this time of need, and a means of receiving this mercy is to draw close to Him, through His remembrance. In a *hadith qudsi*,[44] the Prophet ﷺ, narrated:

> Allah says: "I am to my servant as he expects of Me, I am with him when he remembers Me. If he remembers Me in his heart, I remember him to Myself, and if he remembers me in an assembly, I mention him in an assembly better than his, and if he draws nearer to Me a hand's span, I draw nearer to him an arm's length, and if he draws nearer to Me an arm's length, I draw nearer to him a fathom length, and if he comes to me walking, I rush to him at [great] speed." *(Bukhari, Book of Oneness of Allah)*

Such is the mercy of our Lord! In a similar manner, we can have hope that due to our efforts and our *dhikr*, our babies can also be shown Allah's ﷻ mercy. We know that Allah ﷻ looks after the children of good parents from the example given in the Qur'an, in Surah Al-Kahf (18), in the story of Musa عليه السلام and Al-Khidr during their travels together. The following events are related:

> *Then they proceeded: until when they came to the inhabitants of a town they asked them for food but they refused them hospitality. They found there a wall on the point of falling down but he set it up straight. (Moses) said: "If you had wished surely you could have exacted some recompense for it!"* (Surah Al-Kahf 18:77)

44 A *hadith qudsi*, or sacred hadith, is defined as a hadith that begins with the Prophet ﷺ quoting directly from Allah but it is not a part of Qur'an.

Hardly anybody works for free. Even fewer people do laborious favours for people they do not know. And how many can show kindness to people who have been heartless to them? However, Al-Khidr rebuilt this wall, for free, even though these strangers were unkind to him, for a reason. He explains:

> *As for the wall it belonged to two orphan youths in the town; there was beneath it a buried treasure to which they were entitled; their father had been a righteous man so thy Lord desired that they should attain their age of full strength and get out their treasure: a mercy (and favour) from thy Lord. I did it not of my own accord. This is the interpretation of that which you could not bear.* (Surah Al-Kahf 18:82)

Al-Khidr rebuilt that wall because Allah ﷻ wished to show these two orphans mercy. Allah ﷻ looked after the orphans, through Al-Khidr, because these orphans had a righteous father.[45] They were protected and provided for due to having a virtuous parent. We can hope for the same; if we remember Allah ﷻ, He will remember us, and our children, even in our absence.

This desire to help and provide for our children is why pregnancy is a time when we pamper ourselves. We make time to put our feet up and eat well. Many of us also endeavour to think and act positively. We avoid conflict, anger and stress, all for the benefit of our unborn baby. The health for our bodies becomes a priority, so what of the nourishment of our souls? Pregnancy is also the time to pamper our hearts and be showered with the mercy of our Lord. Therefore, let us strengthen our relationship with Allah ﷻ, remember Him frequently and glorify Him:

45 See Tafsir Ibn Kathir of "and their father was righteous" (Surah Al-Kahf 18:82) which states: "a righteous person's offspring will be taken care of, and that the blessing of his worship will extend to them in this world and in the Hereafter. This will occur through his intercession for them, as well as their status being raised to the highest levels of Paradise, so that he may find joy in them."

Allah is He with whom there is no other god, Who knows (all things) both secret and open; He, Most Gracious Most Merciful. Allah is He with whom there is no other god, the Sovereign, the Holy One, the Source of Peace (and Perfection). The Guardian of Faith, the Preserver of Safety, the Exalted in Might, the Irresistible, the Supreme: Glory to Allah! (high is He) above the partners they attribute to Him. He is Allah, the Creator, the Evolver, the Bestower of Forms (or colours). To Him belong the Most Beautiful Names: Whatever is in the heavens and on earth does declare His Praises and Glory: and He is the exalted in Might, the Wise. (Surah Al-Hashr 59:22-24)

Qur'an for Babies

In our endeavour to mention Allah ﷻ frequently in all aspects of our lives we not only receive His mercy but we also familiarise our babies with the name of Allah ﷻ. Remember that a very alert pair of ears, that go with us wherever we are, are witnesses to all that we utter.

For the little one listening to all that is happening around us, we need to play Qur'an whenever we can: in the car, at home, when cooking and cleaning, when sitting down with a cup of tea. Better still, we can recite Qur'an ourselves. Remember that our baby prefers our voice, above all other sounds, so we should try reciting ourselves, rather than playing tapes or CDs, as much as possible. This is important as it is "live" language that is the key to enhancing early language development. Sitting our children next to a radio or in front of a television does not have the same impact as direct human input during the start of life.[46]

46 Meyerhoff, M. K. (1992), *A Parents' Guide To Enhancing Early Language Development - Perspectives on Parenting, Pediatrics for Parents*

There are no specific chapters or verses of Qur'an mentioned in *hadith* that pregnant women are recommended to recite with regards to benefit to the baby, or the mother (or labour and birth). However, we may like to listen to and recite short chapters from the end of the Qur'an as these are likely to be the first parts of Qur'an that we teach our children, so we can give them a head start by familiarising our baby with these chapters whilst still in the womb. By spending time perfecting or learning Qur'an we are also developing ourselves to be a teacher for our unborn and shaping their sense of hearing to the words of Allah ﷻ.

Some of us may already recite along with our favourite reciter or happily go about doing our daily business reciting. However, others may have preferred just listening, or reciting quietly to themselves, or thinking about the verses without reciting them. For such sisters, we should try to begin reciting aloud as soon as we can, so that it is easy for us when the baby is listening and learning.

For many of us, reciting Qur'an audibly may be difficult, for example those who do not know Arabic or those of us who live with our brothers-in-law, or other non-*mahram* men, who are not permitted to hear us recite or beautify our voices. In order to introduce the remembrance of Allah ﷻ to our babies in an alternative way, we can say our daily *du'a* out loud. This can be the *du'a* for eating, sleeping, dressing, going to the bathroom, travelling etc. If we are able to do this, our baby will hear the frequent mentioning of the name of Allah ﷻ throughout the day, *insha'Allah*, despite us not being able to recite Qur'an ourselves.

For such *Muslimahs* in particular, but also for the rest of us, we can try to get our husbands involved by asking them to join us in our efforts, if they can do so. For example, they can recite *Ayat al-Kursi* (The Verse of the Throne), the last two ayat of Surah Al-Baqarah (2), and the last three surahs of the Qur'an before sleeping.[47] After all, second to the mother's voice, our baby has the greatest affinity for his father's voice, which is also very familiar. Together we can, *insha'Allah*, ensure that it is the mentioning of Allah ﷻ that our baby likes to listen to, over and above all else, including the TV.

Our babies will prefer to listen to whatever is familiar to them. Let us consider what we are familiarising our babies with. What are we subjecting their ears to? "On average, a viewer watches 20,000 commercials each year. If we repeated a page of Qur'an to you that many times, do you think you would memorize it?" writes Muhammad al-Sharif.[48] Imagine how many songs, theme tunes of programmes or adverts become engraved in our babies' minds, even when still in the womb. Compare this with the number of verses of Qur'an we have imprinted on their hearts. Even if we spent a portion of the time that we spend watching TV with Qur'an we would be much more familiar with the words of Allah ﷻ, along with our babies.

---

47 Reciting these before bed is *sunnah.* As for *Ayat al-Kursi*: Narrated Abu Huraira ؓ: Allah's Apostle ordered me to guard the *zakat* revenue of Ramadan. Then somebody came to me and started stealing of the foodstuff. I caught him and said, "I will take you to Allah's Apostle!" Then Abu Huraira described the whole narration and said: That person said (to me), "Please do not take me to Allah's Apostle and I will tell you a few words by which Allah will benefit you. When you go to your bed, recite *Ayat al-Kursi*, (Surah Al-Baqarah 2:255) for then there will be a guard from Allah who will protect you all night long, and *Shaytan* will not be able to come near you till dawn." (When the Prophet heard the story) he said (to me), "He (who came to you at night) told you the truth although he is a liar; and it was *Shaytan.*" (Bukhari, Book on Beginning of Creation)

As for the last two verses of Surah Al-Baqarah, the Prophet ﷺ said, "If somebody recited the last two verses of al-Baqarah at night, that will be sufficient for him." (Bukhari, Military Expeditions led by the Prophet ﷺ)

And the last three surahs of the Qur'an: A'isha ؓ, the wife of the Prophet ﷺ narrates: "Whenever Allah's Apostle went to bed, he used to recite Surah Al-Ikhlas, Surah Al-Falaq and Surah An-Nas and then blow on his palms and pass them over his face and those parts of his body that his hands could reach. And when he fell ill, he used to order me to do like that for him." (Bukhari, Book of Medicine)

48 Al-Sharif, M. (undated), *The Third Parent,* online at www.sunnahonline.com

We need to develop a sincere effort to save ourselves and our children from being amongst those that have lost the Qur'an. We are confining Qur'an to mere wall hangings and picture frames as words that gain most attention as calligraphy and art, not as the Message of Allah ﷻ. Let our families not be of those who wrap up their *masahif* (copies of Qur'an) and let them gather dust on high shelves in our houses, with no place in our hearts or lives. Let us make a sincere effort to live and hear Qur'an daily, to give life to a generation that does the same and more *insha'Allah*.

We can also strive in making the Qur'an affect our hearts by studying it and discovering what Allah ﷻ is saying to us. We can read the translations and commentaries on the Qur'an that are so readily available. Try reading surahs whilst being conscious of their special and specific virtues. If we spend time with Qur'an striving to develop a love and awe of Qur'an, and feel at peace when we hear our voices recite Allah's ﷻ words, then this can also be the effect it has on our children, *insha'Allah*. They will already enjoy the mention of Allah's ﷻ name and His words being frequently on our tongues and in our homes from the day they take their first breath.

Mind Those Ears!

As pregnant women, we tend to have a heightened awareness of what our ears receive. We are increasingly conscious of the fact that soon our baby will hear all that we hear. Therefore, whilst providing the best of words for our babies to listen to (Qur'an and *dhikr*), we also need to ensure that we safeguard our babies, as best we can, by being careful about what their ears receive.

We should avoid both speaking and listening to all that is harmful for our unborn. We need to strive in abstaining from and avoiding foul language, obscene talk and music. Many parents, even non-Muslim parents, shelter their children from bad language, being rude or even using slang. Sadly though, many parents, including Muslim parents, are not careful about harmful music. But we ought to be as Allah ﷻ says:

> *Incite whoever you can among them with your voice, and assault them with your horses and foot soldiers, and become a partner in their wealth and their children, and promise them. But Shaytan does not promise them except delusions.* (Surah Al-Isra 17:64)

This verse is referring to *Shaytan* and has been explained with the statement, "the voice of *Shaytan* is music".[49] Imagine allowing our children to sit and listen to someone who commands them to do evil, all while we passively observe. No parent would do such a thing. Yet most parents expose their babies to the pinnacle and source of evil, *Shaytan*. This may seem an extreme angle on what is seen as the insignificant issue of music. The Prophet ﷺ foresaw that people would make music a harmless entity and he had warned us against it:

> There will be a group of people from my *Ummah*, who will make *zina* (fornication and adultery) and silk,[50] and intoxicants, and musical instruments *halal. (Bukhari, Book of Drinks)*

---

49 See Shihabuldeen Mahmud ibn Abd Allah al-Alusi's, '*Ruh al-Ma'ani fi Tafsir al-Quran al-Adheem wa al-Sab al-Mathani*', 15/111. Mujahid was one of the students of Ibn Abbas, the foremost scholar of tafseer in Makkah and his tafseer of the Qur'an is through revelatory knowledge (Qur'an and hadith) itself, not his own thoughts and opinions. He explains this ayah as referring to music.

50 The wearing of silk is *haram* (prohibited) for men only.

The companions of the Prophet, the generation that followed them (*Tabieen*) and all four Imams[51] regard music to be *haram* (unlawful), therefore indulging in it is sinful and brings the wrath and displeasure of Allah Almighty. As pregnant women, we have two hearts to protect, one of which is fresh and untainted, beating within us, which we desire to keep as pure as can be. Parents recognise that indecent language and swearing is something that is at least distasteful, if not disgusting, and therefore protect their children from such words. Music is no exception.

Having said this, sometimes we are unable to avoid things we should not let our babies hear. This is particularly the case in public, for example the music playing when we go grocery shopping. To try to neutralise these times for our unborn, we can ensure that our own tongues are seeking protection from *Shaytan* and remembering Allah ﷻ. To do this we can say the *ta'awwudh* (أعُوذُ بِاللهِ مِنَ الشَّيطَانِ الرَّجِيمِ which translates as 'I seek refuge with Allah from *Shaytan* the accursed') and *insha'Allah* combat such times that are beyond our control. By doing so our baby is hearing the remembrance of Allah ﷻ over and above the voice of *Shaytan* because in the world of the womb, the mother's voice reigns supreme.

51 Imams Abu Hanifah, Malik, Shafi and Hanbal, who form the foundations of the four schools of Jurisprudence.

It's Never Too Late

We do not always fulfil our goals. This is particularly the case during pregnancy due to the extra demands placed on our minds and bodies. Sometimes we feel that we have not been able to make the most of our pregnancy and think that our unborn may not have had the very best of starts in life. Perhaps we were unable to provide maximal exposure to Qur'an, or we were unable to protect what our bump was listening to. Let us not despair, because it is never too late to begin, or to repair.

It is important to remind ourselves that pregnancy is just the very beginning. Pregnancy is only nine months and the baby can hear for a fraction of this time; after hearing is functional. Once born and if Allah ﷻ wills, our babies will not only be able to hear us but also see and feel us. They can then learn a lot more from the sounds that reach their ears.

For all those accounts of newborn babies knowing portions of Qur'an, if not knowing the entire Qur'an, we should not forget that these children will only have been able to demonstrate their ability once they could talk. As we can see from the psychological findings discussed earlier, it is entirely possible that a newborn would be familiar with and recognise Qur'an. However, this could not manifest itself in a little newborn because the only sound that emanates from a new baby is crying, with the exception of Isa عليه السلام[52] who spoke in the cradle.

It is a year, sometimes two years after birth, before toddlers utter their first words. Between the birth and their first vocalisations, children have the opportunity to hear much more Qur'an than they do in the womb. The time from which the

52 Two other babies are also known to have spoken – see a lengthy hadith in Bukhari, Book of Prophets, which begins "None spoke in the cradle but three..."

baby first hears and the time when they first speak is all time in which they listen and learn - it is not solely during the pregnancy. Continual, sustained learning over a period of around two years gives them much longer to familiarise themselves with and memorise Qur'an.

This is not to discourage us in putting the effort in whilst pregnant but to console those of us who would like to have done more during pregnancy but could not, or did not. This effort does not end with the birth of the baby; rather, it has only really just begun. The year or more we have before our babies begin speaking those first little words and are developing language, we can, *insha'Allah*, expose them to Qur'an regularly, to build upon all the Qur'an they heard whilst in the womb, whether that was a small or great amount.

Once our babies are born it is ever more important to expose them regularly to Qur'an, even when they cannot talk and seem inattentive. It is important because babies recognise sounds that infants, children and adults fail to distinguish. A large body of psychological research has shown that babies can easily discriminate both native and non-native sounds, but by the time they are ten to twelve months old, this ability is lost. Speech perception then becomes similar to adults' ability in that they are only able to easily discriminate native sounds.[53]

What this means is that when very young, Allah ﷻ bestows babies with the ability to accrue a vast range of sounds, which gives humans the ability to acquire any one of the world's languages. However, this ability to acquire any language diminishes and eventually disappears. Of course there is not an absolute loss because we can learn new languages later in life too; it is just

53 For example see Werker, J. F. & Tees, R. C. (1984a), Infant Behavioural Development, (7):49–63.

much, much more difficult. There is a time limit on specifying the sounds that are natural and familiar to our babies beyond which all other sounds, that we do not expose them to regularly, become foreign or even unperceivable.

Based on these findings, we can ensure that our children have a firm grasp of the sounds and pronunciation of the letters of Qur'an (*tajweed*) so that the accurate articulation of these letters, that may not be very easy for us, are no problem for them, *insha'Allah*. This particularly applies if Arabic is not our mother tongue as many of the letters in the Qur'an will not be spoken in our homes and perhaps the only way our children will hear them is by listening to Qur'an. Many of us may need help in perfecting the way in which we read Qur'an and pregnancy would be an ideal time to begin *tajweed* courses to help us. Attending such classes also means that we regularly spend at least a little time every week with Allah's ﷻ words and our unborn hears human voices, and our voice, reciting Qur'an. If we have Qur'an as a part of our lives, we can make Allah's ﷻ chosen language their language.

The Soul

The phenomenon of the soul has always fascinated many yet remains much of a mystery. It is the subject of vast debate that occupies many thinkers, from psychologists and philosophers to the layperson. The nature of the soul is an enigma, because Allah ﷻ has chosen to keep this knowledge to Himself:

> *They ask you about the soul. Say that the soul is from Allah and you have not been given knowledge of it except a little.* (Surah Al-Isra 17:85)

Some of what we do know about the soul is that it is part of the composition of our being, along with our material body, both of which are given whilst in the womb. Allah ﷻ is not only developing the physical bodies of our babies, He also grants our unborn children their souls. The Prophet ﷺ expanded on this and told us that the soul is breathed into a baby, whilst in its mother's womb, when it is 120 days old:

> A human being is put together in the womb of the mother in forty days, and then he becomes a clot of blood for a similar period, and then a piece of flesh for a similar period. Then Allah sends an angel who is ordered to write down his deeds, his livelihood, his (date of) death, and whether he will be blessed or wretched. Then the soul is breathed into him.
> *(Bukhari, Book of Beginning of Creation)*

With the advances in science the concept of the soul in the foetus has recently taken an interesting slant. The current trend is to explain or try to understand phenomena, including that of the soul, in rational, scientific, tangible terms, based on experimental evidence.

Despite knowing that *only* Allah ﷻ knows, we often try to make sense of the *ruh* and have our theories about it and what differentiates a body with and without a soul. One of the assumptions held today is that the mind is related to the soul. More specifically, it is a common belief that thinking and physical phenomena (such as electrical activity of the brain and facial expression/emotion) have direct relationship with the soul. This is a statement made by many modern philosophers and psychologists, in terms of the mind-body debate and the concept of consciousness respectively.

However, this assumption is baseless with no proofs, yet many of us have subscribed to this belief, be it implicitly or explicitly. In terms of the *ruh* in the foetus and its relationship to physical or bodily development, science has revealed facts such as the brain being developed enough by eighteen weeks to trigger the heartbeat and that the baby jumps at loud noises. All this very human behaviour has developed before 120 days and before a soul is placed within the body. The foetus does not become more human-like or more alive in a physical sense when it has a soul, based on what we know today.

From these observations we can conclude that the placing of the *ruh* does not have a direct bearing on the physical development of the baby that we know of, as yet. This is not a reason for alarm or doubt because there is no reason to think that the *ruh* has such an effect or relationship with the body. Neither Allah ﷻ, nor His Messenger ﷺ have alluded to such a link. Perhaps we think that the *ruh* directly impinges on the body because our primary conception of the relationship between the *ruh* and the body is with death. We know that death is when the body ceases to function and we know that death involves the removal of the soul. Try balancing this with the fact that the soul is also taken out every night, when we sleep. Allah ﷻ says in the Qur'an:

> *It is Allah who takes away the souls at the time of their death, and those that do not die during their sleep. He keeps those souls for which He has ordained death and sends the rest for an appointed term. Indeed, in this are signs for those who think deeply.* (Surah Az-Zumar 39:42)

> And the Prophet ﷺ said: "Sleep is the brother of death." *(Mishkat, Characteristics of Heaven and its People)*

At stages during sleep we do not have our souls. They are removed from our bodies yet none of us would argue that we are dead or lifeless or somehow different in terms of our biological make-up during sleep. When asleep we can talk, some even walk and our brains sustain their normal functions, as do the rest of our bodies – all with the absence of a soul. Therefore we know that the *ruh* does not necessarily render physical changes in the body with its addition or removal. This is worth remembering when thinking about the soul being placed in the foetus. Thus the words of Allah ﷻ are shown to be true: He has not revealed knowledge of the soul except a little!

Calculating the Big 120th Day

Many pregnant *Muslimahs* regard the time when their babies will be visited by an angel to grant it a soul as very special. We wait for the day when our foetus becomes a complete person. So how do we know when this day is?

The medical profession dates pregnancy from the first day of the last menstrual period. Using this method, pregnancy lasts for forty weeks, and at conception we are medically regarded as already being two weeks pregnant! This dating technique is referred to as "gestation". In Islam pregnancy is dated from the day we conceive and this is referred to medically as "weeks since conception" or "weeks since fertilisation".

The 120th day occurs at around seventeen weeks after conception. For women with twenty-eight day cycles, this is roughly nineteen weeks from the first day of our last menstrual period. For those of us with shorter or longer cycles it is not as simple as this and we need to try and calculate when we ovulated. We then count 120 days from this date.

Ovulation occurs twelve to sixteen days before a period. Therefore, if we count back two weeks from our missed period date we can estimate the time we are likely to have conceived, although knowledge of the exact date of conception lies with Allah ﷻ alone.

Du'a for a Righteous Soul

> Then Allah sends an angel who is ordered to write down his deeds, his livelihood, his (date of) death, and whether he will be blessed or wretched. *(Bukhari, Book of Beginning of Creation)*

The Prophet ﷺ told us that not only is our baby granted a soul, an angel also writes down their destiny. The fate of our children is written whilst we are carrying them. The angel is told to write whether our child will be fortunate or whether it will be deplorable. Every parent prays for a blessed child and we dread to give birth to a wretched soul. We fear the notion of nurturing and loving a child, our own child, who will ultimately present neither themselves nor us with any good, a child that is destined for doom. Therefore, the placing of the soul is something we must focus on by making *du'a* that Allah ﷻ grants us righteous children, who have books of deeds that will make them proud and successful on the Day of Judgement. Only by making *du'a* can we hope for this:

> Nothing but supplication averts the decree, and nothing but righteousness increases life. *(Tirmidhi, Book of Destiny)*

We also have the satisfaction of knowing that the *du'as* we make for our children are readily accepted and so we should ask Allah ﷻ for our children plentifully:

> There are three prayers which are accepted without any uncertainty; they are: the prayer of one who has been oppressed: the prayer of a traveller; and the prayer of parents for their child. *(Abu Dawud, Prayer: Detailed Injunctions about Witr)*

These *du'as* are best made early, at least from the time we know we are pregnant, as there is another saying of the Prophet ﷺ that relates that some aspects of destiny are written even before the soul is placed, at only forty or fifty days (six to seven weeks) after conception:

> When the drop remains in the womb for forty or fifty (days) or forty nights, the angel comes and says: 'My Lord, will he be good or evil?' and both these things would be written. Then the angel says: 'My Lord, would he be male or female?' and both these things are written. And his deeds and actions, his death, his livelihood; these are also recorded. Then his document of destiny is rolled and there is neither addition to nor subtraction from it. *(Muslim, Book of Destiny)*

A good *du'a* to make is the *du'a* of Zakariyya عليه السلام which he made in his old age while his wife was barren, and to which Allah سبحانه وتعالى responded and gave him Yahya عليه السلام as a son:

رَبِّ هَبْ لِي مِن لَّدُنْكَ ذُرِّيَّةً طَيِّبَةً إِنَّكَ سَمِيعُ الدُّعَاءِ

O my Lord! Grant me from You a good offspring. You are indeed the All-Hearer of invocation. (Surah Al-'Imran 3:38)

There is also the *du'a* of Ibrahim ﷺ for which Allah ﷻ granted him Isma'il ﷺ:

رَبِّ هَبْ لِي مِنَ الصَّالِحِينَ

> *My Lord! Grant me (offspring) from the righteous.* (Surah As-Saffat 37:100)

We may worry about how physically perfect our child will be and how healthy they may or may not be. This concern for their physical well-being and the *du'as* we make for them to be free from disease, defect and disability should be at least matched by equal concern for their soul and whether they will be righteous. After all, what is the good in a beautiful perfectly formed baby, free from illness, if the heart is dead? Our baby's soul is something we can surely pray for as Allah ﷻ has told us that He hears all that we ask of Him:

> *When My servants ask you (O, Muhammad) concerning Me, I am indeed close to them. I listen to the prayer of every supplicant when he calls upon Me.* (Surah Al-Baqarah 2:186)

Furthermore, as encouragement and comfort, we know that Allah ﷻ actually loves us to ask of Him:

> Nothing is dearer to Allah than one's supplication to Him. *(Ibn Majah, Book of* Du'a*)*

We should therefore always be asking of Allah ﷻ. He wants us to ask of Him and we can ask none but Him. This is why we should be making a concerted effort to make sincere *du'as* to Allah ﷻ for all things, however big or small, however impossible or implausible they may seem to us. There is only Allah ﷻ who provides for us and answers our *du'as* and so we can only turn to Him. The Prophet ﷺ told us that our *du'a* will not go unanswered and he ﷺ also told us that we can never ask too much or too frequently:

> One should beg one's (Lord) with a will and full devotion, for there is nothing so great in the eye of Allah which He cannot grant. *(Muslim, Book on the Remembrance of Allah)*

There are particular times when *du'as* are accepted such as the last third of the night (*tahajjud* time):

> Our Lord, the Blessed and Exalted, descends every night to the heaven of this world when the last third of the night is still to come and says, "Who will call on Me so that I may answer him? Who will ask Me so that I may give him? Who will ask forgiveness of Me so that I may forgive him?" *(Bukhari, Book of Prayer at Night)*

> The Prophet ﷺ was asked, "What supplication finds the greatest acceptance?" He answered: "A prayer offered in the middle of the latter part of the night and after the prescribed Prayers." *(Tirmidhi, Book of Supplications)*

Allah ﷻ, our Lord and Creator, the Most High, mercifully descends to our heaven every single night solely to see who is in want of anything, saying, "Ask of Me and I will grant it to you". Who is there in this world that is free of need and want? Who is there that should not be begging for blessed children? Many of us will wake to make yet another trip to the toilet, be up contemplating whether to go for a stroller, travel system or three-wheeler or worrying about our waters breaking in the supermarket. This is the time when we can also beg Allah ﷻ for righteous offspring, for an easy pregnancy, labour and birth, and for Allah ﷻ to make us from amongst the best of parents.

III.
Labour and Birth

"Childbirth isn't just something that women go through, it's something that changes them as individuals, something that shows them their vulnerability and strength, something that teaches them about themselves."[54]

This is the big day we all anxiously await. As pregnant women we have mixed feelings about labour and birth because it is the day when, *insha'Allah*, we finally see and hold the baby that we have been carrying for nine months. However, in order to meet our babies we have to go through childbirth…the little somebody we really want to see has to come after something we really do not want to go through!

Many of our conceptions about labour and birth, as first-time mothers, stem from other women's accounts, television and films. However, no woman knows what labour and birth are like until she has experienced it for herself. Not only that, but no woman knows what *another* woman's labour and birth are like. Even the same woman can have varying pregnancies, labours and births with each child she bears. Our preconceptions of the day we count down to are often far removed from what we are to actually face.

The most important way in which childbirth actuality departs from expectation for most of us is the idea that this is to be a horrific experience. It is often the opposite. Allah ﷻ has exquisitely designed the female body to give birth. Many a mother will testify that the day she gave birth to her new baby was one of the most exhilarating and wonderful days of her life. Giving birth to a baby is something that is not beyond us physically, emotionally or mentally because:

> *On no soul does Allah place a burden greater than it can bear.*
> (Surah Al-Baqarah 2:286)

---

54 Moorhead, J. (1996), *New Generations: 40 Years of Birth in Britain,* National Childbirth Publishing Trust, HMSO, London

Birth Plan

Some of us take pains over our birth plans and some of us would rather not bother with them. It might be the thought of the actual labour and birth that deters us from thinking about the birth plan, or it may be that we think that a birth plan is not of great importance. Is a birth plan a fantastical wish list that will be ignored by the staff that deliver the baby? Is it unwise to try and plan a birth when nobody knows what will happen? Do we even have any specific wants and want-nots or do we just want to have a baby?!

Some of us may feel more confident in relying on those attending to us to make any decisions for us, particularly if they are professionals such as doctors and midwives, as we find comfort in their judgement and medical opinion as compared to our own. There are many times that this proves true. However, research has also clearly shown that the more empowered and in control women feel about labour and birth, and the more involved they are in the decision making, the better they perceive their birthing experience.[55] Instead of feeling as though procedures were carried out without our consent, or feeling that we would have preferred a different course of action or treatment, we can make informed choices about how and where to have our baby.

Most of our decisions about labour are best made antenatally, particularly in the form of a birth plan. Birth plans can be written in advance, without pressure, in the comfort of our own homes. This may not be the situation we find ourselves in when decisions need to be put into action during labour. When labour has begun we are not likely to have the time, enthusiasm, energy or focus to

55 Leeman, L., Fontaine, P., King, V., Klein, M. C., Ratcliffe, S. (2003), American Family Physician, p1109-1115

explore and assess what we would prefer or avoid. Having specific requirements and wants written down (if we have any), before we go into labour, can be a great help as it saves us speaking to husbands or medical staff when concentrating on contractions! Birth plans help ensure that what we feel to be important does not go ignored and is always accounted for, as far as possible.

Birth plans can also be effective tools of communication between labouring women and their midwives. They are particularly useful in conveying the needs that may be of paramount importance to Muslim women that non-Muslim women may not share. There has been a growing recognition of our specific needs resulting in a recent report focusing solely on the experiences of Muslim women, entitled "Experiences of Maternity Services: Muslim women's perspectives".[56] Midwives are aware of the general concerns and requirements of a *Muslimah* but are also sensitive to us as individuals, understanding that Muslim women are not a homogenous group. Each of us has our preferences and this will be reflected in how and where we wish to give birth. It can therefore be useful to have personal preferences conveyed to our midwives, rather than letting them guess or assume what we need.

But what decisions will we have to be making? When reading up on the different aspects of labour and what occurs during the birthing process, we encounter various stages that require a choice by the mother on which procedure or course of action suits us best. Some considerations for the birth plan include: who we would/would not like to be present with us for the birth or stages of labour/birth and how the baby is to be welcomed. If we have our babies in hospital we can request *halal* meals and state whether we want to be in a ward or a private room after we have the baby. Birth plans ensure that these decisions do not have to

56 Ali, N., Burchett, H., Sivagnanam, R. (2004), *Experiences of Maternity Services: Muslim Women's Perspectives,* London, Maternity Alliance

be made on the spot. Many of the choices we need to make in labour are often very important to us and the right decisions will make our experience of labour far more favourable in hindsight.

When planning a hospital birth, we can also request individual rooms after the birth, if and when they are available. Some hospitals will charge a fee for this though it can be money well spent for the privacy we would gain. If we are in a ward, rather than a room of our own, we can still gain privacy by drawing the curtains around the bed, for example for breastfeeding or during visiting times when other men are around. The privacy issue has been highlighted as one that is central to Muslim women by the Maternity Alliance and is one that we should expect to be upheld by the maternity ward. It can help immensely to take the time to speak to one or two members of staff to explain ourselves.

Sometimes things do not go quite as we imagine and so a birth plan is not a pre-written script for what is to happen. By allowing for the possibility that we may need to compromise on, or even abandon, certain parts of our birth plans we prepare ourselves mentally for the possibility that we may change our minds on the day or things may not go as we imagine. For example, if a request for female only staff had been made and there comes a point in labour when a doctor is needed immediately, and the only doctor available is male, we would be seen by him, despite stating in the birth plan that we wanted female only staff. For such reasons it's best to keep birth plans flexible. By writing something such as: "I would like female only staff, as far as possible at all times, unless I have no other option" will prepare both ourselves and our midwives better than "I do not want any male staff". This flexibility also sounds more favourable to our midwife and makes her life easier! It is also worth discussing a draft of the birth plan with a midwife before formalising it in the pregnancy file.

In order to make things easier for ourselves, and our midwives, it helps to make any wishes about the birth clear by having thought about what we want and need. However, if birth plans are still not our cup of tea, or we do not get round to writing a birth plan and labour comes along, or if we decide to throw everything in the birth plan out of the window on the big day then let us find comfort in knowing that no matter how much we plan, Allah ﷻ has already planned, and He is the best of Planners! This is a frame of mind that all pregnant *Muslimahs* must always have: an understanding that everything is in Allah's ﷻ hands and the best we can do is put our trust in Him and rely on Him alone. There is no might or power except with Allah ﷻ and we are grateful for all that He gives.

Homebirth

The mere mention of "homebirth" can be enough to alarm most women, and even more so their poor unsuspecting husbands, "What? Delivering the baby at home?! You have got to be joking!"

Homebirth is more of a serious consideration for some women who find the busy, clinical nature of hospitals, bustling with uniformed staff and lots of other labouring women, a little off-putting. To such women, the idea of being in a relaxed and familiar space, in the comfort of their own homes and enjoying their own privacy seems a luxury in comparison.

The issue of private space has even greater significance for a *Muslimah*. Childbirth is a time when dignity and *'awrah* are of great concern and this concern is settled to a greater degree when opting for a homebirth, rather than choosing to have our baby in a hospital. On the other hand, some women are happy with giving birth in hospital and take reassurance from the hospital setting. Home may be the last place we would like to give birth, particularly if we have many other people in the house.

There are obvious concerns in opting to have a baby at home. Homebirth is really only an option in healthy pregnancies where there are no hints of any risks. Any signs of possible complications and women are transferred to hospitals, either during their pregnancies or during labour. If we are discouraged to have a homebirth on medical grounds then it is advisable to respect professional opinion as it is not worth taking any risks.

Many women (and their husbands!) have fears about having homebirths. Primarily, it is the risk of complications. We may ask ourselves, is a homebirth safe? In normal pregnancies, the answer is yes; "Healthy low risk women who wish to deliver at home have no increased risk either to themselves or to their babies."[57] It is also reassuring to know that all midwives bring resuscitation equipment and drugs to deliver the placenta and to stop heavy bleeding, should they be needed after the birth. Midwifery care alone is sufficient for normal pregnancies and birth.

Other concerns mothers-to-be may have regarding home births include the possibility that we will change our minds when labour begins. Women choosing a homebirth have the generous option of going to the hospital at any stage during labour, or changing their minds at any time during the pregnancy. However, deciding to stay at home when we stated we would have a hospital birth is not really a possibility as nobody has planned or prepared for the home delivery.

Another common worry can include the horrifying thought of having to clean up after the baby is born. This would have never crossed a pregnant woman's mind when choosing a hospital birth. *Alhamdulillah*, midwives bring along items that would be

---

57 Ackermann-Liebrich, U. et al. (1996), British Medical Journal, 313:1313–1318

used in a hospital setting, such as super-absorbent bed pads etc, to manage the mess. The only downside is not being able to use the towels that some hospitals offer after the birth that we needn't worry about washing!

Midwives also conduct a home visit towards the end of the pregnancy, if we are considering a homebirth. This includes assessing our home for suitability and ease of use in delivering a baby, issuing items in order to prepare for the delivery and planning what needs to be arranged in the room we plan to give birth in. A big plastic sheet on the floor/bed is included in this so that everything can simply be wrapped up and thrown away. Other items that need to be prepared or purchased are the same as what is needed for a hospital birth, such as cotton wool and sanitary towels.

There are advantages and disadvantages to both home and hospital births. One potential down-side of opting for a homebirth includes the fact that certain forms of pain relief can only be administered in hospital and they are therefore not available as options when considering a homebirth. Only entonox and pethidine are available whilst labouring at home and if we decided to have an epidural we would have to go to the hospital.

It is also worth knowing that women expecting their second, or subsequent, babies make up a greater percentage of those opting for a homebirth. This is often because a homebirth needs a certain degree of confidence in the natural process of childbirth and this is strengthened by past birthing experiences. So, even if this is a first pregnancy where homebirth is not really an option that is being considered, it may well be that it is a very real consideration in future pregnancies, *insha'Allah*.

Packing for the Birth

Towards the end of pregnancy we are advised to begin preparing items for the birth of our baby. Along with our own changes of clothes, birth plan and various personal items, this preparation also includes clothes and nappies for the baby, along with a car seat in most cases. Some women refrain from buying these items for superstitious reasons that warn not to purchase or prepare anything for the unborn. Allah ﷻ says:

> *No soul knows what it will earn tomorrow.* (Surah Luqman 31:34)

It is only Allah ﷻ who knows what has been destined for us and for our babies. We place our trust in Him, ask for His protection and help, and accept His will. However, we also take the advice of the Prophet ﷺ and do our part in preparing and taking caution, together with placing our trust in Allah ﷻ:

> One day Prophet Muhammad ﷺ noticed a Bedouin leaving his camel without tying it. He asked the Bedouin, "Why don't you tie down your camel?" The Bedouin answered, "I put my trust in Allah." The Prophet ﷺ then said, "Tie your camel first, then put your trust in Allah." *(Tirmidhi, Description of The Day of Judgement)*

In a similar vein, though we rely solely on Allah ﷻ, it is advisable to prepare for the day we are to give birth, even if this means preparing a detailed list that someone else will be able to follow in order to pack the necessary items for us. This is ideally someone who we are not relying on for support (they will be busy fulfilling their role of supporter *insha'Allah*) and someone that we can rely on, as far as possible, to be around and be able to find all that we need in our absence. If we do not have someone that can fit this role then it is much easier to gather items that we need during labour and for the birth before labour is imminent.

For anybody who has not packed a labour bag before, it is surprising what we need. In addition to the usual things that all women are recommended to take along to hospital or have ready at home for a homebirth, we can consider taking along the following items:

1. Qur'an

We may want to listen to the Qur'an during labour and to play some to the newborn. We may not be able to recite ourselves and by the time the baby is born we will not be reciting as we will have begun postnatal bleeding. Having Qur'an playing during labour gives us something beautiful to concentrate on, by listening to what Allah ﷻ has revealed. This focus diverts attention from what is happening and turns out to be excellent pain relief! Some hospitals have CD players, others do not so if we plan to take along the Qur'an to listen to on tape or CD then it is worth making sure that we will have something to play it on where we are labouring. Most hospitals are happy for women to bring along their own tape/CD players.

2. *Du'a*

The *du'a* we would like to make can be written down and packed. We might have other people asking us to make *du'a* for them whilst we are in labour as our *du'a* will *insha'Allah* be accepted during our time of need. We can also write out these requests, along with the *du'a* we would like to make for ourselves, as we might not be able to remember them during labour. It is much easier to read them off a piece of paper than to try and recall them all. We may even need someone to read them to us and we can repeat after them, be it silently in our hearts.

3. Items for Prayer

If we use prayer beads (*tasbeeh*) or prayer mats then we may also need them, along with a compass. Ensure that our birth partner is confident in using the compass as it is likely that they will be the ones having to use it. If we pray in a special garment then we might like to have this packed too. These items may also be useful for our birth partner, particularly if we are giving birth in a hospital which does not have a prayer room near the delivery room.

4. Clothing

When choosing which clothes to give birth in it is worth carefully selecting what to wear. Comfortable, easy to pull on/off trousers or skirt are a must. These can be coupled with a long front opening top that covers down to the knees so that if and when we do not have trousers on, we still remain well covered. A front opening top will also allow us to breastfeed our baby *insha'Allah* with minimal exposure. If we plan to have the baby delivered straight on to the stomach[58] then a shirt may be the best option as they can be opened fully, otherwise whatever top we are wearing can be pulled up instead.

When expecting a hospital birth it is worth pre-selecting which head-covering and *jalbab*[59] to wear whilst travelling to give birth. Whatever is easy and quick to put on, with no fiddling involved is probably best. For example an extra large shawl, a long *khimar*,[60] or a pull-on scarf (that does not need to be pinned or tied) along with a front opening *jalbab* (like a coat), with a minimal number of fastenings, would be ideal.

58 Rather than having the baby examined first, we can choose to have the baby delivered and given directly to us.

59 A long, loose garment worn over clothing, when outside the home, to conceal our figure entirely.

60 A one-piece, circular head covering with a hole cut out for the face.

Let us remind ourselves that this is not a time in which we can excuse ourselves of the command from Allah ﷻ to cover our entire body appropriately (huge bump included) with a *jalbab* when in public.[61]

5. *Miswak*

A combination of our unique hormone levels together with the increased blood supply can cause sensitive, swollen or bleeding gums. It is therefore particularly recommended for pregnant women to regularly use *miswak*:

> It (i.e. *miswak*) is a purification for the mouth and it is a way of seeking Allah's pleasures. *(Bukhari, Book of Fasting)*

We may have already begun to rely upon *miswak* (also known as *siwak*) throughout pregnancy, even more than our pre-pregnancy days, because gum and teeth problems are very common during pregnancy and toothpaste can make pregnant women feel sick. A *miswak* is far easier to use than a toothbrush with toothpaste and is therefore particularly helpful when labouring. We may like to use *miswak* after having been sick, to help us wake up when are feeling sleepy during the advanced stages of labour (yes, this can happen!), before reciting Qur'an or praying, or as something to bite on! *Miswak* is also great when we are extremely busy with a brand new baby and can even be used whilst breastfeeding.

---

61 "O Prophet, tell your wives and daughters and the believing women to draw their outer garments around them (when they go out or are among men). That is better in order that they may be known (to be Muslims) and not annoyed. Allah is ever Forgiving, Merciful." (Surah Al-Ahzab 33:59)

6. Dates

And the pains of childbirth drove her to the trunk of a palm-tree: she cried (in her anguish): "Ah! Would that I had died before this! Would that I had been a thing forgotten and out of sight!" But (a voice) cried to her from beneath the (palm-tree): "Grieve not! For thy Lord hath provided a rivulet beneath thee; And shake towards thyself the trunk of the palm-tree: it will let fall fresh ripe dates upon thee." (Surah Maryam 19:23-25)

Allah ﷻ gave Maryam *alayhas salaam*, dates when she gave birth to Isa عليه السلام. The Prophet ﷺ also recommended eating dates. We now know some of the medical benefits of doing so, specifically for pregnancy, labour, childbirth and postnatal conditions. Studies have shown that dates contain "stimulants which strengthen the muscles of the uterus in the last few months of pregnancy".[62] In addition to helping to activate the delivery process, dates are a quick source of energy, which is just what you need during the last trimester and in labour. During the early stages of labour, dates will not fill us up and so we will not feel the need to vomit due to a full stomach in later phases of labour.

Dates are also recommended after childbirth as they are generally restorative and a high-energy food with particular benefit for the nursing mum. Dates contain potassium, glycine and threonine, which activate the milk hormone prolactin. Al-Shahib and Marshall[63] state: "Dates may be considered as an almost ideal food, providing a wide range of essential nutrients and potential health benefits."

---

62 Omar-Muhammad, R. (2003), Dates: The Crown of Sweets, *The Muslim Woman*, 4(7):26

63 Al-Shahib, W. & Marshall, R. J. (1993), International Journal of Food and Science Nutrition, 54(4):247-259

7. *Zam zam*

We might also like to have some *zam zam* for the birth because "The water of *zam zam* is whatever it has been drunk for." (Ibn Majah, Book of Rights of Hajj). Whatever *du'a* we make before drinking *zam zam* is granted, so we can ask for strength, pain relief, healing, helping breastfeeding and so on.

We can also have *zam zam* packed in the hospital bag for weeks, or stored for months out of the fridge and it has the miraculous quality of still tasting just as it would taste if you were stood drinking it next to the *Ka'ba*.

Birth Partner

"Continued psychological support during labour reduces the need for analgesia (pain relief), makes caesarean sections less likely and improves the outcome of labour for both mother and baby."[64]

Most women would like somebody to be with them as they give birth to their baby. Often, this is our mum or sister, or we may like our husbands to be there. Evidence clearly indicates the benefits of having a birth partner, in addition to the medical staff present. The support of a laywoman results in shorter labours, less intervention and the mother reporting greater confidence and self-esteem.[65] However, contrary to the fashion of today, the presence of the father at his child's birth is of questionable benefit.

Having men involved in the birthing process is not the *sunnah* nor is it the practice of most cultures. A lady called Salma

---

64 Schott, J. & Henley, A. (1996), *Culture, Religion and Childbearing in a Multiracial society - A handbook for professionals,* Oxford; Boston, Butterworth-Heinemann

65 Hofmeyr, G., Nikodem, V., Wolman, W. et al. (1991), British Journal of Obstetrics and Gynaecology, 98:756-63; Sosa, R., Kennel, M., Klaus, M. et al. (1980), New England Journal of Medicine, 303 (11):597-600

attended *Rasulallah*'s ﷺ wife, Khadija, when she gave birth to all six of their children.[66] He ﷺ would also send women to attend to women in labour. We also have a detailed example of 'Umar رضي الله عنه doing the same when he was *Khalifah*. One night 'Umar رضي الله عنه came upon a tent on the outskirts of Madinah with a man sitting outside the tent. He heard a woman inside the tent and inquired about her. The man outside the tent revealed that his wife was alone and about to give birth. 'Umar رضي الله عنه immediately went home and asked his wife, Umm Kulthum bint 'Ali, to help the woman about to give birth. Umm Kulthum went in the tent to help the lady in labour and 'Umar رضي الله عنه sat outside with the lady's husband and cooked a meal for them. Whilst he was still cooking, Umm Kulthum called out, "Oh Leader of the Believers, congratulate your friend, Allah has blessed him with a boy."[67]

There is a lot to learn from this example. 'Umar رضي الله عنه, the one on whose tongue and heart Allah has placed truth,[68] thought it more beneficial for the labouring woman to have assistance than to give birth alone. Not only this but he also judged that her husband should not assist her, rather a woman, Umm Kulthum, would be better suited to the role of birth partner. The men waited outside.

Also note that the couple whom Allah سبحانه وتعالى blessed with a new baby boy that night were travellers; they were strangers in Madinah and did not know anyone there. This meant that the woman about to give birth had never met her birth partner before. We can understand from this account that it is not important that the person we choose to support us during labour and birth

---

66 Muhammad Ibn Sa'd (1995), *The Women of Madina*, translated by Aisha Bewley, Ta-Ha Publishers

67 Related in Anwar Al-Awlaki, *Umar Ibn Al-Khattab - His Life and Times,* Al-Basheer Publications

68 Abu Dawud, Book of Tribute, Spoils and Rulership

is someone that we know and love. Communities worldwide often have women in the neighbourhood who are known to accompany labouring women. This is not always the expectant woman's own mother, sister or grandmother, but a woman who has experience in helping during childbirth. This is because it is the nature of the aid that is provided that is key, not who it comes from. The world over, it is known that women are best suited as birth partners.

It may amuse us to know that when the proposal of fathers being encouraged to attend births was made in 1960, it was abandoned due to reservations such as fathers fainting and disagreeing with the doctors![69] Though amusing, these initial concerns may not be too far from the truth in cases (though this can also be equally applicable to some women!). Research on fathers' experiences of labour and birth is limited but there is some concern that men may inhibit women in labour and the whole experience may have adverse effects on the father.[70] Some pregnant women may feel that they have to support and encourage a hesitant partner to attend the birth because it has now become the norm for the father to witness the birth of his baby.

Fathers-to-be often do not anticipate the psychological and emotional impact of childbirth. Pregnancy and birth is stressful for men too and the greatest levels of stress are found in men who attend births, particularly in those men who feel they are not fulfilling their role, or when they feel pressured in attending the birth.[71]

From the father's perspective, it has also been suggested that attending the birth of his baby may hinder the development of

69 Brown, A. (1982), Fathers in the Labour ward: Medical and Lay Accounts. In: McKee, L., O'Brien, M. (eds) *The Father Figure*, Tavistock Publications, New York

70 Hall, J. (1993), Nursing Times, 89(46):69-71

71 Johnson, M. P. (2002), J Psychosom Obstet Gynaecol., 23(3):173-82

his bond with the baby, slow down his partner's labour, alter his perception of her and have a negative effect on sexual attraction beyond birth. Jeremy Laurance, health editor for The Independent, goes further: "Mothers are discovering the secret of a good birth is having another woman present. The loss of female support in childbirth and its replacement by men could lie behind the soaring Caesarean rate, which has doubled in 20 years. A review of 15 research trials involving almost 13,000 women published in the Cochrane Library, the biggest source of evidence-based health care in the world, has demonstrated a female supporter is the best guarantee of a natural birth."[72]

Laurance's article, bravely titled, "How to avoid a Caesarean: take along a female friend for the support the father cannot provide" focuses on hiring a female supporter, a doula. Doulas are not medically qualified but are trained to provide encouragement, praise, support, coping strategies and to represent the mother's views to medical staff. The strategy behind using a doula is one that we can all employ. For some couples, the support that would otherwise be provided by a doula may come solely from the father, but for others it will be a woman who is in the best position to provide this support. The most important requirement is that the birth partner is one who is a source of comfort and encouragement, solely having our best interests at heart and one whom we need not worry about during our time of need. Often, the perfect person for this important role is our mother or sister.

Having said that, for many women today, our husbands may be the ones who are the support and strength we rely on during difficult times. This is likely to be especially true of the typical modern day nuclear family that no longer has strong links with

72 Laurance, J. (2003), "How to avoid a Caesarean: take along a female friend for the support the father cannot provide", The Independent 24/9/03

extended family. Many of us do not live with our parents or siblings. The relationship we may have with friends may be close but it may not be enough for us to have our best friend attend the birth of our baby. In such cases our husband may be the one we want by our side. Husbands are often good at asking questions and expressing our views and wishes to medical staff when we have not quite got our heads together, but they are generally not very good at nursing! A possible good indicator of how useful our husband will be as a birth partner is how well he copes when we are unwell or when upset, or better still, when we are both ill and stressed at the same time!

The benefits for the labouring woman in having their partner present have yet to be conclusively demonstrated and women have been proven to be more suited to the role of supporter. Having said this, most of us will want our husbands to at least be in the vicinity when we give birth. However, we can also choose not to have him present at the time of delivery, starting from when the baby begins to emerge, even if he is with us throughout labour and returns once the baby is born. As soon as the baby is born the new father can come in and hold the baby and call the *adhan* softly in his newborn's ear. This provides fathers with an important role in a process that they can otherwise feel helpless in.

Secondary to our reliance on Allah ﷻ alone as Helper and Protector and our comfort in this fact, what is important is that the support we may want and need is there, and that this comes from the right person, even if it is from our midwives alone.

The "Due" date

The expected due date (EDD) is a pregnant woman's big day. The EDD is like a stereotypical wedding day in many ways: months of preparation, anxiety, excitement, and the big count down to a moment that we know will change us forever. However, unlike weddings, EDD's are generally not the actual big day: only four per cent of babies are born on their due dates![73]

Lots of women have their hospital bags and nurseries ready far in advance of their EDD. Many of us imagine having the baby early, secretly desiring that the big day will come soon after our hospital bag is packed. We may even have managed to convince ourselves that we are certain to have the baby by a particular date. Unless we have had much exposure to women going beyond their due dates, we rarely entertain the thought that we might not have the baby in our arms on that big day we all count down to. Even for those who know that the majority of first babies arrive after their EDD, we can somehow think that will not be us, just as we do with all situations that we would rather not see ourselves in – it's the infamous "it'll never happen to me" syndrome!

Some women do have their babies "early", some babies are even born prematurely (seven per cent of births are early), but it is very common for babies to be born "late". This is especially true for first time mums; more first-timers go past their due date than not. The terms "early" and "late" deserve to be qualified as babies are born exactly on a prescribed day when Allah ﷻ wills them to be born, and at the precise time that was written for them:

73 MIDIRS (Midwives Information and Resource Service - in collaboration with NHS Centre for Reviews and Dissemination) (Undated), Informed Choice for Professionals - Prolonged Pregnancy, No. 12. Bristol, MIDIRS.

Allah knows what every female (womb) doth bear by how much the wombs fall short (of their time or number) or do exceed. Every single thing is before His sight in (due) proportion. He knows the Unseen and that which is open: He is the Great the Most High. (Surah Ar-Ra'd 13:8-9)

How can this time that Allah ﷻ describes as "being in His sight in due proportion" possibly be described as being "early" or "late"? It is the calculated due date that is too early or too late in comparison to when the baby is meant to be born. Let us take this attitude as comfort when worrying about when our baby will join our world, particularly when we go over our EDD.

Even if we have not yet reached the days leading up to our EDD, the thought, "I just can't wait to have this baby!" is quite likely to run through our minds – several times! After all, Allah ﷻ has described mankind as hasty:

Man is a creature of haste: soon (enough) will I show you My Signs; then ye will not ask Me to hasten them! (Surah Al-Anbiya 21:37)

To go beyond our due date is normal. There is nothing abnormal with us, or our baby, and there is no need to feel shy, embarrassed or uncomfortable in having gone past our EDD. The calculated EDD is a bit of guesswork as methods of predicting due dates rely on very regular periods and assume ovulation to have occurred in the middle of the cycle. They also ignore factors such as the origin of the mother, miscarriage preceding the pregnancy, stress, anxiety and research that identifies first time mothers as having longer pregnancies. In other words, due dates are not hard and fast rules for when a baby must arrive by. They are merely a rough guide. So, hang in there - this baby will come - they do not stay in there forever, no matter how cosy they may be!

If we do go past our calculated due date then it may be of comfort to know that after forty-one weeks, six out of ten women have their babies in the next three days and nine out of ten have them in the next week.[74] It can also be of great help to keep busy. Take these last few days without a newborn in the house as precious days to see friends and family (that live fairly close by!), to listen to tapes/CDs in peace, to stock up on food and other shopping in the house so that there is one less thing to do once the baby arrives *insha'Allah*, and to sleep!

We can also tell people that we will call them when we have any news, rather than them phoning us. If we ask people not to call everyday then we can save ourselves the pain of having to repeatedly say that we have not had the baby yet, which can be frustrating or upsetting – or both!

Let us make *du'a* that Allah ﷻ makes us content and satisfied with his decree, and to ask for patience in accepting what He has planned for us. Allah ﷻ knows when our baby will be born and this knowledge is only with Him. We prepare for this day, whenever that day may come, whilst being fully aware that we have no clue when that day will be!

Du'a during Labour

Many of us feel specially protected and directly looked after by Allah ﷻ during pregnancy. We may have often found our *du'as* being readily accepted. During labour, in our final hours of pregnancy, this bounty is extended to its full as our *du'as* are answered as never before. We implore Allah ﷻ with a reliance on Him alone,

74 MIDIRS (Midwives Information and Resource Service - in collaboration with NHS Centre for Reviews and Dissemination) (Undated), Informed Choice for Professionals - Prolonged Pregnancy, No. 12. Bristol, MIDIRS

knowing that He is the One driving and controlling the entire process of birth. We seek His help during our time of need as there is no one that we can turn to other than Him. This creates a unique and powerful sincerity that guarantees acceptance.

> *Or, Who listens to the distressed (soul) when it calls on Him, and Who relieves its suffering.* (Surah An-Naml 27:62)

The faith, hope and dependence on Allah ﷻ during labour are difficult to match at any other time in life. It is an invaluable opportunity for *du'a*. Naturally, we beg Allah ﷻ to help us through labour and birth but we can also ask for much more:

> One should appeal to Allah with firm determination for nothing is too much or too great for Allah to give. *(Muslim, Book of Oneness of Allah)*

Let us not think it is too much to ask - Allah ﷻ can make our births easy! It may be a good time for *du'a* during the early stages of labour as it is less intense and we may be more able to focus on making *du'a*. Contractions last no longer than a minute or so and come quite regularly with rather pain-free minutes in between them. This means we can rest between them, make *du'a* and prepare for the next one. We can even use *du'a* as a means of getting through each contraction. During the earlier stages of labour we can also try to make *du'a* centred on all things other than giving birth and remember those who asked us to make *du'a* for them during this time. In the later stages of labour we may not be able to think past anything other than birth. However, some women report far less or even no pain when at the pushing stage and are very focused so this may prove to be an amazing time for *du'a* or *dhikr*. Remember that these need not be said aloud, though controlling our breathing by taking Allah's name, or even crying "*Allahu akbar*" out loud may also be a great way to manage!

Something we may like to try during labour is sending salaam to the Prophet ﷺ[75] because every time we say this Allah ﷻ sends on us multiple blessings:

> He who invokes one blessing upon me, Allah will shower ten blessings upon him. *(Muslim, Book of Prayers)*

> He who invokes blessings upon Allah's Messenger ﷺ once, Allah and His Angels shower seventy blessings upon him. *(Mishkat, Sending Salaam on the Prophet ﷺ and its Virtues)*

There are many *du'as* that the Prophet ﷺ made during times of need (labour is one such time!). It will be particularly helpful to have such *du'as* written down as we are likely to find it easier to read something, or have it read to us, rather than recalling it from memory. There are many *du'as* we can use to help us through childbirth. Though these *du'as* are not specifically for labour they encompass the circumstances that commonly arise in labour. A handy summary of the *du'as* in Arabic translated into English, along with the transliteration, is included in the appendix and can be copied and packed ready for when labour begins.

---

75 An example of invocating blessings and peace upon the Prophet of Allah ﷺ:

اَللّٰهُمَّ صَلِّ عَلٰى مُحَمَّدٍ وَّ عَلٰى آلِ مُحَمَّدٍ كَمَا صَلَّيْتَ عَلٰى اِبْرَاهِيْمَ وَّ عَلٰى آلِ اِبْرَاهِيْمَ اِنَّكَ حَمِيْدٌ مَّجِيْدٌ

Allahumma salli 'ala Muhammad wa 'ala ali Muhammad kama sallayta 'ala Ibrahim wa 'ala ali Ibrahim innaka hamidun Majid

O Allah, bless Muhammad and the family of Muhammad as you had blessed Abraham and the family of Abraham. Verily you are the Praised, the Glorious.

When planning for an easy labour and birth let us also remember this *hadith*:

> Whoever wants Allah to answer his prayers during difficult times, should supplicate to Him more and more in times of ease. *(Tirmidhi, Book of Supplications)*

So we can begin to sincerely make *du'a* now, whilst we are still pregnant, for Allah ﷻ to help us during labour and birth. We can also ask friends and family to make *du'a* for us too because our *du'as* for each other when apart are answered:

> The supplication that gets the quickest answer is the one made by one Muslim for another in his absence. *(Abu Dawud, Prayer: Detailed Injunctions about Witr)*

> Safwan ibn 'Abd Allah reported, "I visited Abu Darda's house in Syria. I did not find him there but Umm Darda was present at the house. She asked, 'Do you intend to perform *hajj* during this year?' I replied, 'Yes.' She said, 'Do supplicate Allah for us, for Allah's Messenger ﷺ used to say, "The supplication of a Muslim for his brother in his absence is accepted when he makes a supplication for blessings for his brother, and the commissioned Angel says, '*Ameen*, May it be for you too!'"'
> I went to the market and met Abu Darda ؓ and he narrated a similar report from Allah's Messenger ﷺ." *(Muslim, Book Pertaining to the Remembrance of Allah)*

Salah in Difficult Times

So woe to the worshippers. Who are neglectful of their Prayers. (Surah Al-Maun 107:4-5)

In the hours and minutes leading to the emergence of our much-awaited baby, there is a gift from Allah ﷻ that we already have that we must never neglect. This is the gift of faith. An essential part of our *iman* is *salah* and when we lose our *salah* we lose a fundamental aspect of faith:

What lies between a man and disbelief is the abandonment of prayer. *(Muslim, Book of Faith)*

Many women in labour find *salah* difficult. There may also be other times in late pregnancy that can affect our *salah*. We may think that it is beyond us to pray. However, we should understand that in such circumstances prayer can be modified in order that we are able to offer our *salah*, even during times such as childbirth. *Salah* is always obligatory, even during war, whilst fighting on the front lines, and in times of fear, so much so that Allah ﷻ specifically describes how to pray during such times in the Qur'an.[76] We are punishable for abandoning prayer intentionally, no matter what situation we are in.

In times of difficulty Allah, Most Merciful, allows us to pray in a way that is safe and manageable for us. For example, if we cannot stand and pray, then we can sit down. If we cannot sit, then we can lie down:

'Umar ibn Hussain said, "I had some physical problem so I asked the Prophet ﷺ about the prayer and he said, 'Pray standing; if you are not able to, pray sitting; if you are not

76 See Surah An-Nisa 4:102-103

> able to, pray (while lying) on your side.'" *(Bukhari, Book of Shortening the Prayers)*

When sitting or lying down and offering *salah,* we bend forward a little for *ruku'* and bend further for *sajda.* If we cannot make any movements then small movements of the head will suffice.

It is probably wise to be firm on offering *salah* as soon as the time begins as we do not know if we will be able to pray if we delay it. We may advance quickly into the next phase of labour. We may even end up having the baby and then enter into *nifas* (postnatal bleeding).

During labour, we can lose track of time or we may forget to pray so it is also a good idea to ask someone to remind us about *salah*, and to encourage and help us to pray as soon as *salah* time starts. Those around us may not realise that *salah* is still obligatory on us so it is worth discussing this with our birth partner or whoever may be around at the time of delivery towards the end of our pregnancy.

A suggestion for making *salah* easier and more manageable is to stick to the bare essentials of prayer, the most obvious of which is to only offer the obligatory units of prayer and to leave the rest if we are unable to pray them.

An important note on *salah* when in labour regards purity. *Wudhu* is an essential precondition of *salah* and we should try to fulfil this as far as is practicable. There is no need to drench each body part in water or pass running water over it, just a little water to wet the hands and spread over each relevant part is enough. If we have trouble making *wudhu* by ourselves we can ask someone else to help us or even do it for us. They can bring us a bowl of water and a towel if we can not make it to the bathroom, particularly if this means climbing stairs. If we do not have help and nobody to bring us water we can do *tayammum*:

If you find no water, then take for yourselves clean sand or earth, and rub therewith your faces and hands. (Surah An-Nisa 4:43)

Tayammum is when no water is used and instead earth, sand, soil or stone is used to attain purity. To perform *tayammum* we are to strike the ground or walls with both hands once, then wipe the palms of the hands over the face then wipe the hands and arms up to the elbows.

A further prerequisite of *salah* is covering the necessary parts of the body. Ensure that all our hair (fringe included!) and arms (right up to the wrist) are properly covered as exposure of these body parts for more that a few seconds nullify prayer. In the later phases of labour and birth we may find that we have to pray whilst sitting or even lying down. If this is the case then a sheet over our body will be fine, even if we have very little or no clothing on underneath.[77]

We should try our best to face the *qiblah* but if we are unable to judge which direction to pray, or we really do not know where the *qiblah* is and have nobody to ask, then we should face whichever way our hearts feel inclined and this prayer need not be repeated at a later date.

Let us not think that *salah* is beyond us during difficult times. Think of examples of people who have prayed in situations far more trying than ours. When 'Umar ﷺ was suffering from the stab wound that led to his death, he was unconscious. He woke up and said, "The prayer, by Allah! Verily, there is no share in Islam for whoever abandons the prayer."[78] He then prayed while his wound was bleeding, virtually on his deathbed, but he did not abandon his *salah*.

---

77 Abu Huraira was asked, "May a man pray in one garment?" He said, "Yes." The man then said to him "Do you do that?" and he replied, "Yes, I pray in one garment while my clothes are on the clothes-rack." (Muwwatta, Prayer in Congregation)

78 See Ibn al-Jawzi's, *The Characteristics of the Most Excellent* 2/131

What better way to begin this tremendous new phase in life, in the final hours and minutes of carrying a baby, than to turn to Allah ﷻ together? What better way to seek His help than prayer?

> *Rasulallah* ﷺ said, "The first matter that the slave will be brought to account for on the Day of Judgment is the prayer. If it is sound, then the rest of his deeds will be sound. And if it is bad, then the rest of his deeds will be bad." *(Tirmidhi, Book of Prayer)*

Pain Relief

> *In pain did his mother bear him, and in pain did she give him birth.* (Surah Al-Ahqaf 46:15)

Allah ﷻ has described pregnancy and birth as a difficult time. We undergo a time of need, hardship and trial whilst carrying our baby and during childbirth. Allah ﷻ, in His infinite wisdom, has willed this to be so. It is not easy because it is not meant to be! These difficulties we go through in bearing children are a part of why mothers have such an exalted status:

> From Abu Buraidah that he was with Ibn 'Umar and a Yemeni man was making *tawaf* (circling) of the House carrying his mother on his back saying, "I am her humble camel; where her camel would have gotten frightened I will not." Then he said, "O Ibn 'Umar! Do you think that I have repaid her?" He said, "No, not even for a single moan that escaped her during childbirth." *(Bukhari, A Code for Everyday Living: Repaying the Parents)*

In this narration Ibn 'Umar singles out childbirth, signifying the weight of giving birth in Allah's ﷻ eyes. We may not understand why, but we must accept Allah's ﷻ will in that having a baby is wonderful, yet it has its difficulties. In order to bring some ease on the day we meet our baby, it is healthy to recognise that our birthing experience will involve pain. Having said this, birth is a natural process and Allah ﷻ has designed our bodies, and our babies, perfectly in order to cope. As Muslim women we also find comfort in a promise from Allah ﷻ; to know that this pain or discomfort we feel is never more than what we can bear:

> *On no soul do we place a burden greater that it can bear.* (Surah Al-Baqarah 2:286)

This applied equally to women that lived before birth became a medical procedure, when epidurals and drips did not exist; at a time when mothers relied solely on Allah ﷻ when giving birth, just like Maryam *alayhas salaam* did when she gave birth to her son, Isa عليه السلام, under a palm tree, on her own, with nobody by her side.[79] There is comfort not only in this, but also in knowing that for every difficulty we undergo, there is a hidden surprise:

> Never is a believer stricken with discomfort, hardship or illness, grief or even with mental worry that his sins are not expiated for him. *(Muslim, Book of Virtue, Good Manners and Joining of the Ties of Relationship)*

Alhamdulillah, today many of us have the choice of how and where we would like to give birth, how to manage labour and various options for pain relief. We do not have to do it alone. We can also, if we wish, take measures to reduce anxiety and pain. When we think of pain relief many of us will automatically think medication or drugs. This is not necessarily true as there are

79 See the sub-section on Dates in the chapter titled, 'Packing for the Birth'.

alternatives for those of us who prefer a "natural birth". A natural birth is one that avoids medical intervention, including avoiding the use of pain relieving drugs.

For those of us opting for a natural birth, or simply wanting to avoid the use of drugs, there are several, effective alternative methods of pain relief that we can consider. These include having a warm bath or shower, aromatherapy, using a TENS machine and focusing on controlling our breathing. Many of the options available are ones that women turn to naturally, whether they opt for pain relieving drugs or not, without prior deliberation, prompting or advice. Examples of these include finding comfortable positions, being massaged and using various methods of relaxation and distraction.

The option for pain relief for a natural birth may not sound very powerful in comparison to the offer of an epidural that has the potential (though no guarantee) of removing all pain and feeling, but the trend today of opting for a natural birth has its basis in multiple benefits. The advantages of a natural birth include faster recovery for the mother and the baby not being exposed to any drugs, which provides better foundations for feeding and bonding.

Some women prefer to avoid a natural birth. A few women are only able to face the thought of labour and birth with the aid of an epidural. This is due to women having different pain thresholds and ways in which they react to and cope with pain. Pain has a purely psychological element, together with its physical factors, which is why a fear of labour pain, and the anticipation that this will be unbearable, worsens the experience of childbirth and increases the perception of pain that a woman feels. The more we feel we are able to cope the better we bear the pain.[80]

---

80 Lowe, N. K. (2002), American Journal of Obstetrics and Gynecology, 186:S16-24

This is also why support from a suitable birth partner proves very valuable; significantly reducing the need for intervention. For some women this also means the physical aid of pain relieving drugs. We have not been forbidden pain relief and it is fine to take - if and when we need it.

However, we should be fully aware that any form of pain relief has its advantages and disadvantages. Most mothers would agree that they would prefer to avoid, as far as possible, anything that will harm themselves, particularly their babies. This is an obligation on us as Muslim women. We should therefore understand that all forms of intervention carry risks. In certain situations the risk of not using an intervention is greater than the risk posed by the intervention. *Alhamdulillah*, sometimes obstetric intervention significantly shortens labour, eases pain, relieves distress or even saves lives, if Allah wills.

It is common, however, for intervention to be used aside from medical emergencies, contrary to what we may imagine. Often we find that we enter a stage in labour (which actually is just before it is nearly all over!) where we feel we cannot cope any longer and are ready to take any, and every, possible form of pain relief under the sun. In this far from ideal state of mind, with cervix fully dilated and baby in our pelvis, we forget that when an intervention is used, without purposeful medical benefit, there are further risks that we, and our baby, could face if we opt for intervention. For example, some forms of intervention have a high incidence of concurrent use, such as women who have a forceps or a ventouse delivery being more likely to need an episiotomy (though an episiotomy reduces the likelihood of tears).[81] Complexities such as these may affect the options we consider or adopt in managing pain during labour.

81 Bodner-Adler, B., Bodner, K. Kimberger, O., Wagenbichler, P. & Mayerhofer, K. (2003), Journal of Reproductive Medicine, 48(4):239-42

Many women are offered various forms of pain relief during labour and we may find ourselves in such a situation. It is often too late to think rationally and objectively about pain relief and its use (or anything else!) when labouring. We may therefore think about it beforehand and come to a conclusion on our preferences, perhaps stating them in our birth plan. We might like to consider different forms of pain relief for the varying stages of labour, or have certain stages with no intervention. For example, some women decide only to have medicinal pain relief during the more intense aspects of a prolonged labour and otherwise opt to manage the rest of the course of labour naturally. Of course, childbirth is unpredictable and we may need to forgo our decisions but if we already have firm ideas on what we do/do not want when giving birth then we are more likely to adhere to these during the birth.

If we decide not to use any pain relief and we find ourselves going back on this decision when it comes to crunch time, our birth partner can be a great help. They can support our decision when they feel that we do need some form of pain relief and be a source of encouragement when they see that we are doing well without it. *Insha'Allah* our birth partner is someone that can still focus and be objective even when we may not be, ensuring that the consequences of our decisions during labour are measured.

Though some women prefer not to think too much about labour and birth beforehand, it might be an idea to read up on pain relief, without examining details of labour. This is often recommended as all forms of pain relief work in different ways and have different effects. When it comes to our time of need we can have an idea about what we would like to use, rather than have the decision made for us, without us realising the impact of what we receive. Take, for example, gas and air or entonox. Though it is not yet known to affect the baby, entonox can have adverse effects on the mother. Some women find that they feel dizzy, sick, light-headed, confused or unable to concentrate on labour. In fact, gas and air only "takes the edge off the pain" and many attribute this relief to factors such as the controlled deep breathing that is required when self-administering entonox, having something to focus on, something to control and having a distraction (such as something to bite or hold onto when using entonox). This is a possible explanation of the results in a study which reports no difference between the pain relief given by entonox and ordinary compressed air in early labour.[82]

Whatever our decision on pain relief, we know that Allah ﷻ is the Best of Planners. If He wills that we take some form of pain relief, undergo some intervention or that we have a C-section, we, as believers, accept His will. Having a baby with some form of pain relief, be it drug-based or not, or via a C-section, or with the use of any other intervention, is no more or less an admirable feat than a natural birth. Having a baby is spectacular, no matter how it happens. Our status as a mother, as one who has given birth, is not affected or determined by whether or not we have an epidural, or by using a birthing ball or by giving birth whilst squatting. Sure, childbirth is no small event, but the outcome, the end result of a precious new baby, is the same, no matter how and where the birth occurred or how long the labour lasted. Any mother who decides against pain relief and finds she uses it should not belittle herself or her decision. Any mother who gives birth with no form of pain relief only does so with Allah's ﷻ leave and permission because all that anybody goes through is from Him. We praise Allah ﷻ whatever happens, and are grateful to Him, always.

---

82 Carstoniu, J., Levytam, S., Norman, P. et al. (1994), Anesthesiology, 80:30–5

The First Cry – Curse you Shaytan!

Why do babies cry when they are born? The Prophet ﷺ has given us the answer:

> There is none born among the offspring of Adam, but *Shaytan* touches it. A child therefore cries loudly at the time of birth because of the touch of *Shaytan*, except Maryam and her child. *(Bukhari, Book of Prophets)*

As our bump grows and we become more attached to our baby, we begin to feel increasingly concerned by the above *hadith*. The thought that *Shaytan* "gets his hands" on our baby, even before we have been able to hold them in our arms horrifies us. The desire to protect our baby from all harm can enlighten us on the fact that *Shaytan* is ever present. Perhaps, for once, when we think of this *hadith*, we truly recognise *Shaytan* as our enemy. In our everyday lives we are often too lax when it comes to *Shaytan*, even though Allah ﷻ says:

> *Verily, Shaytan is an open and manifest enemy to mankind.* (Surah Yusuf 12:5)

> *Verily Shaytan is an enemy to you: so treat him as an enemy. He only invites his adherents that they may become Companions of the Blazing Fire.* (Surah Fatir 35:6)

An enemy is someone we should constantly be wary of, and have our defences up and ready for, but we hardly remember that *Shaytan* is even there! This creates the most dangerous type of enemy; one we don't even realise is out there, not only watching and waiting, but in full force.

The minute that a baby enters this world he is faced with *Shaytan*. He is there witnessing the birth, ready to meet every newborn. We have to be there to counteract him. This we can do in two ways. Firstly, we can seek refuge in Allah ﷻ from *Shaytan*, and ask our husbands to join us in this *du'a*:

> Abu Huraira رضي الله عنه said, "The Prophet said, 'No child is born but that *Shaytan* touches it when it is born whereupon it starts crying loudly because of being touched by *Shaytan*, except Maryam and her Son.'" Then Abu Huraira recited: "*And I seek refuge with You for her and for her offspring from the outcast Shaytan.*" (Surah Al-'Imran 3:36)" *(Bukhari, Book of Prophets)*

The second way is to say the *adhan* when our baby is born as the *adhan* drives *Shaytan* far away:

> *Shaytan* hears the call to prayer, he runs away to a distance like that of Rawha' (a distance of thirty-six miles from Madinah) *(Muslim, Book of Prayers)*

We can also continue to seek protection for our newborn babies through a *du'a* the Prophet ﷺ used to make for his grandsons, Hasan and Husain: "Your forefather (i.e. Ibrahim) used to seek refuge with Allah for Isma'il and Ishaq by reciting the following: 'O Allah! I seek refuge with Your Perfect Words from every devil and from poisonous pests and from every evil, harmful, envious eye.'" (Bukhari, Book of Prophets):

أَعُوذُ بِكَلِمَاتِ اللَّهِ التَّامَّةِ مِنْ كُلِّ شَيْطَانٍ وَهَامَّةٍ وَمِنْ كُلِّ عَيْنٍ لَامَّةٍ

Note here that the Prophet ﷺ specifically mentions the evil eye and so we know that the evil eye is true. Furthermore, Allah ﷻ says:

قُلْ أَعُوذُ بِرَبِّ الْفَلَقِ. مِنْ شَرِّ مَا خَلَقَ. وَمِنْ شَرِّ غَاسِقٍ إِذَا وَقَبَ. وَمِنْ شَرِّ النَّفَّاثَاتِ فِي الْعُقَدِ. وَمِنْ شَرِّ حَاسِدٍ إِذَا حَسَدَ.

Say: I seek refuge with the Lord of the Dawn. From the mischief of created things; From the mischief of Darkness as it overspreads; From the mischief of those who practise secret arts; And from the mischief of the envious one as he practises envy. And from the evil of the envier when he envies.
(Surah Al-Falaq 113:1-5)

We can even begin the fight against *Shaytan* before conception:

بِاسْمِ اللَّهِ، اللَّهُمَّ جَنِّبْنَا الشَّيْطَانَ، وَجَنِّبِ الشَّيْطَانَ مَا رَزَقْتَنَا

If anyone of you, when intending to have sexual intercourse with his wife, says: In the name of Allah. O Allah, keep us away from *Shaytan* and keep *Shaytan* away from what You provide us, and if the couple are destined to have a child (out of that very sexual relation), then *Shaytan* will never be able to harm that child. *(Bukhari, Book of Marriage)*

We are unable to reverse the fact that *Shaytan* will touch our newborn because all the children of Adam have this fate, with the exception of Maryam *alayhas salaam* and Isa عليه السلام,[83] but we can be sure to begin the fight against him on behalf of our children, right from day one. Let us also continue to be vigilant and aware of his tricks and plots and regularly seek refuge for ourselves, and our babies, for indeed the plan of *Shaytan* is weak:

So fight against the allies of Shaytan, the plan of Shaytan is indeed weak. (Surah An-Nisa 4:76)

83 "There is none born among the offspring of Adam, but *Shaytan* touches it. A child therefore cries loudly at the time of birth because of the touch of *Shaytan*, except Maryam and her child." (Bukhari, Book of Prophets)

The Placenta and Umbilical Cord

Believe it or not, once we have delivered our much-awaited babies, childbirth is not over. After the baby is born, the body expels the placenta that has been the life-source of the foetus. The placenta has the umbilical cord attached to it, and the cord is on the baby. If we are having the baby in hospital then not only do we want to take the baby home, we also need to remember the cord and the placenta! Detached from the baby of course! Why? It is a part of the human body that ought to be carefully buried, like any other, when it becomes detached from the rest of the body.

The placenta is routinely retained by those who deliver the baby, for all births, in order to check that it is intact. Therefore, it is not a problem for us to take it home or to keep it. All we need to do is ask them to set it aside along with the umbilical cord. It is also useful to provide the midwife with a strong bag or container to store the afterbirth in. Ensure that whatever is used can be sealed. As a guide to selecting the size of container required, it is useful to know that the placenta is about 20-25cm (8-10in) in diameter and weighs around 1kg (2.2lb). Remember to also have a spade handy in the garden if this is where the placenta and cord are to be buried. We should advise our willing volunteer to dig deeply enough so that it is out of the reach of animals (the last thing a postnatal woman wants to do is bury the placenta herself!).

A further possible consideration for the birth of our baby with regards to the afterbirth is the timing of cutting the cord. Allah ﷻ has made the umbilical cord a means through which our babies change from life in the womb to life in our world. Babies are born attached to the cord and placenta so that there is not an immediate demand on their lungs to begin breathing. This is achieved by the placenta retaining some of the baby's blood once we have given birth. The retained blood carries oxygen along the cord to the baby. The baby then gradually reduces its reliance on the cord blood and begins using its own circulatory system. It only takes a few minutes and the cord then stops pulsating.

It is common practice today for the cord to be clamped and cut immediately after birth rather than waiting for it to stop pulsating, thus forgoing this gradual transition to our baby's lungs functioning independently. There are good reasons to choose to transgress this norm, particularly as there is no evidence to support that early cord clamping is beneficial. Rather, early cord clamping poses specific risks, as does any intervention in childbirth. The World Health Organisation states, "Late clamping (or not clamping at all) is the physiological way of treating the cord, and early clamping is an intervention that needs justification."[84]

In contrast, benefits of delaying the cutting of the cord until it has stopped pulsating include reducing iron deficiency anaemia[85] due to an increased number of red blood cells.[86] A further and rather special benefit of not clamping and cutting the cord immediately is that it gives the family precious time together, moments that are unforgettable and irreplaceable. This time is otherwise used in the midwife undertaking routine procedures such as assessing and weighing the baby. This can all wait and be done after the time we have to bond with our amazing newborn.

84 The Department of Reproductive Health and Research (RHR), World Health Organisation's 'Care in Normal Birth: A Practical Guide Report' (1997). 'Timing of Cord Clamping' is section 5.5 in 'Care During the Third Stage of Labour'.

85 Emhamed, M. O., van Rheenen, P. & Brabin, B. J. (2004), Tropical Doctor, 34(4):218-22
Michaelsen, K. F. et al. (1995), Acta Paediatrica, 84:1035-44
Pisacane, A. (1996), British Medical Journal, 312:136-137
Grajeda, R. et al. (1997), American Journal of Clinical Nutrition, 65:425-31

86 Papagno, L. (1998), Acta Physiologica, Pharmacologica et Therapeutica Latinoamericana, 48(4):224-7

Many standard procedures in childbirth are questionable as to whether they are in place merely for reasons of convenience and cost-effectiveness for the health industry or if our best interests are the primary focus. For example, many hospitals advise women to have their labour induced within forty-eight hours if their waters have broken, yet the Scientific Advisory Committee of the Royal College of Obstetricians and Gynaecologists (RCOG) recommends that the maximum time given should be ninety-six hours. We need to be aware that routine procedure does not have to be our procedure. We can say no to our medical recommendations or instructions if we wish to do so. Though it is not necessary, nor appealing to some parents, one can examine all the various routine procedures and find that refusing the procedure is as equally sound as accepting it, if not wiser in some cases, provided that we have a sound basis for doing so. One such instance may include the time when the cord is cut, and Allah ﷻ knows best.

Welcome Baby!

After giving birth to the baby we long for, we hold them close, looking at them in amazement. The very first moments of their lives form very treasured memories. Women often have a rollercoaster of emotions which can be very different to what we had imagined feeling at the time of delivery (especially if it's a boy when we were convinced it was to be a girl or vice versa!). We may experience anything from relief, awe, to gratitude. We may be in tears, or laughing or just wanting to sleep. Whatever our reaction, these are memorable moments.

During these special first minutes and days of life outside the womb we introduce our babies to the world, as Muslim babies. There are Islamic etiquettes of receiving the newborn and an outline of the various *sunnan* we should fulfil is given below.

1. *Adhan* and *Iqamah*

It is *sunnah* to softly say the *adhan*[87] in the right ear and the *iqamah*[88] in the left ear of the newborn. New parents are often naturally moved to saying "*Allahu akbar*" (Allah is the Greatest) when they first see and hold their brand new baby. It is a beautiful way in which to greet our newborn as the first word they hear as soon as they enter this world is the name of Allah ﷻ and our faith in Him. *Rasulallah* ﷺ would call the *adhan* in the ears of newborn babies, even if they were not his children. So we can ask another male member of the family, perhaps the grandfather, or our imam, to call the *adhan* if it is not the baby's father doing so. Whoever calls the *adhan* needs to be available as soon as the baby is born as it

87 Adhan is the call to prayer (see below). Abu Rafi reported that: "I saw Allah's Messenger ﷺ call the *adhan* in the ear of al-Hasan ibn Ali." (Abu Dawud, Book of General Behaviour)
4 x★ اللّٰهُ أكبَرْ *Allāhu Akbar* (Allah is the Greatest)
2 x أشهَدُ أن لاَ اله إلاَّ الله *Ash-hadu allā ilāha illallāh* (I bear witness that there is no god except Allah)
2 x أشهَدُ أنَّ مُحَمَّدً الرَّسُولُ الله *Ash-hadu anna Muhammadur rasūlallāh* (I bear witness that Muhammad is the Messenger of Allah)
2 x حَيَّ عَلَى الصَلاَة *Hayya 'alas-salāt* (Make haste towards prayer)
2 x حَيَّ عَلَى الفَلاَح *Hayya 'alal-falāh* (Make haste towards success)
2 x اللّٰهُ أكبَرْ *Allāhu akbar* (Allah is the Greatest)
1 x لاَ اله إلاَّ الله *Lā ilāha illallāh* (There is no god except Allah)
★Maliki's say this twice only

88 This is the second call to prayer, given immediately before the start of the prayer. Hasan ibn Ali ﷺ reported that Allah Messenger ﷺ said: "Who has a child born then he says *adhan* in his right ear and *iqamah* in the left then he will not be influenced by Umm as-Sibyan." (This is a kind of fear that can affect the child.) (Bayhaqi, Shu'ab al-Iman, see ﷺ8916). The *iqamah* is almost like the *adhan* except that after حَيَّ عَلَى الفَلاَح *Hayya 'alal-falāh* (Make haste towards success) the following is said twice: قَدْ قَامَتِ الصَلاَة *Qad qāma tis-salat* (Stand for prayer)

is recommended that the first words that reach their ears are the *adhan*. Remember also that the *adhan* drives away *Shaytan* who is also present at the birth.[89]

2. *Tahneek*

This is to lightly rub a softened or well-chewed date on the newborn's tongue. The wisdom in this *sunnah* can be seen in a study[90] reporting that placing a sugary substance in the newborn's mouth reduces their crying, pain sensation and heart rate. To use dates, especially the ajwa dates of Madinah, is *sunnah*.[91] Some parents choose to use honey. Note that honey is now labelled as being unsuitable for babies under twelve months old and so we may prefer to adhere to the *sunnah* of using dates, rather than opting for honey.

3. Naming the baby on or by seventh day

The *sunnah* is to have the baby named by the seventh day. Remember that the day that the baby is born is counted as day one, not day zero as our midwife/health visitor will describe it

89 "There is none born among the offspring of Adam, but *Shaytan* touches it. A child therefore cries loudly at the time of birth because of the touch of *Shaytan*, except Maryam and her child." (Bukhari, Book of Prophets)

90 Haouari, N., Wood, C., Griffiths, G. & Levene, M. (1995), British Medical Journal, 310:1498-1500

91 Anas reported that: My mother said to me: "Anas, none should suckle him until you go to Allah's Messenger ﷺ tomorrow morning." And when it was morning I carried him (the child) and went along with him to Allah's Messenger ﷺ. He said: "I saw that he had in his hand the instrument for the cauterisation of the camels. When he saw me, he said: 'This is, perhaps, what Umm Sulaim has given birth to.' I said: 'Yes. He laid down that instrument on the ground. I brought that child to him and placed it in his lap and Allah's Messenger ﷺ asked Ajwa dates of Madinah to be brought and softened them in his mouth. When these had become palatable he placed them in the mouth of that child. The child began to taste them. Then Allah's Messenger ﷺ said: 'See what love the Ansar have for dates.' He then wiped his face and named him 'Abdullah." (Muslim, Book Pertaining to the Merits of the Companions of the Holy Prophet ﷺ)

and that the Islamic day begins at *Maghrib*. There is no basis for the superstition that the baby's date and time of birth should affect the name given to the baby. We have simply been instructed to find good Muslim names for our children, with a good meaning. No special rituals or ceremony need accompany naming.

4. *Aqiqah*

This is to offer sacrifice of an animal (or two for boys), on or after the seventh day after birth. Any animal that is used for the sacrifice at *Eid* is also suitable for an *aqiqah*. This is a *sunnah* and we are not obliged to fulfil it. If we are unable to have an *aqiqah* we should fear no harm to ourselves nor to the babies. If we would like to fulfil a blessed *sunnah* and have an *aqiqah*, it need not be done urgently after the birth of our baby. We have the option to delay it to a more convenient time, particularly if we need time to recover from the birth and adjust to life with a new baby rather than hosting/organising an *aqiqah*.

5. Shaving the baby's head

All hair on the head, if there is any, is to be shaved on the seventh day after birth and not before. Note that the seventh day is calculated by counting the day that the baby is born as day one. So if our baby is born on Friday, the following Thursday will be the seventh day. This is the *sunnah* for both boys and girls. The hair should then be weighed and its equivalent weight in silver is to be given as *sadaqa* (charity).

Alongside the various *sunnahs* of welcoming the newborn, there are additional manners in which we can greet our new baby, as soon as they are born, that have been found to be beneficial for both our babies and ourselves. This includes encouraging skin-to-skin contact immediately after the birth. If Allah ﷻ wills us to have a normal vaginal birth then we can request that our baby be delivered straight onto our abdomen. Some women do not like the idea of having their baby lie on them or next to them before they have been wiped clean, or prefer to have them weighed and assessed before holding their baby. However, research has highlighted the benefits of early skin contact and this is a practice now encouraged for all mothers.

Newborn babies find comfort lying with their mothers, listening to the familiar rhythm of their heartbeat. A new baby cannot regulate its own body temperature very well and therefore benefits by lying on its mother as this helps maintain its temperature.[92] This skin contact also helps to regulate their heartbeat and breathing,[93] makes them less agitated and helps them to sleep better.[94] This has also been proven to be beneficial for premature babies.[95] Babies that have skin contact as opposed to lying alone have also been found to cry significantly less.[96] Our baby can be wrapped in a towel and remain undressed as they lie on our tummies,[97] listening to the *adhan* in the first few moments of their life in this world, without any fear of harm to them.

This beautiful time of holding baby is also one that encourages the development of a strong bond between mother and baby. Babies are surprisingly alert when born, particularly in the first hour or so after the birth, which proves to be valuable in initiating breastfeeding. Amazingly, studies have demonstrated that when mother and baby are enjoying skin-to-skin contact, if

---

92 Christensson, K. et al. (1992), Acta Paediatrica, 81:488-493

93 Fohe, K., Kropf, S. & Avenarius, S. (2000), Journal of Perinatology, 20 (5):311-315

94 Messmer, R., Rodriguez, S., Adams, J. et al. (1997), Pediatric Nursing, 23 (4):408–414

95 Rosenblatt, J. S. (1992), Acta Paediatrica, 81:488-493

96 Christensson, K. et al. (1992), Acta Paediatrica, 81:488-493

97 This is also another advantage of choosing a front opening top to give birth in. We, or whoever is by our side, can quickly open the top before the baby is delivered on to us.

they are left undisturbed, babies search and root out the breast. This helps to promote successful first breastfeeding.[98] These two factors of early skin contact and early breastfeeding have been shown to aid the bond between mother and baby as well as longer-term breastfeeding,[99] unless the baby is drowsy from the effects of any pain relieving injections we have had during labour such as pethidine. It is also interesting to note that babies whose mothers had received pethidine did not suck at all,[100] indicating that a reliance on such pain relieving injections is best avoided as far as possible.

In these precious moments after birth, we can use the time to lie back with our new baby in our arms, just looking at each other, talking to them, letting them know that they are still with mummy.

The Postnatal Period

Along with packing a hospital bag, preparation for labour and birth for the Muslim woman includes reading up on *nifas* or postnatal bleeding. Postnatal bleeding has been designed by Allah ﷻ to allow the body to expel any remaining blood, mucus and placenta left in the uterus after birth.

There is immense ingrained myth and ignorance surrounding postnatal bleeding amongst many Muslim women from various backgrounds. For the modern day *Muslimah* who has left behind "back-home-culture" and its baggage, we may go to a different extreme and reject all notions of a postnatal period, with the exception of the bleeding and its immediate consequences (such

98 Righard, L., Alade, M. O. (1990), Lancet, 336:1105-1107

99 Widstrom, A. M. et al. (1990), Early Human Development, 21:153-163

100 Righard, L., Alade, M. O. (1990), Lancet, 336:1105-1107

as not being able to pray and fast). We aim to resume normal everyday life as soon as we have had the baby and deny that our bodies have been through a colossal episode. Rather than resting and recovering we race back into everyday life and activities, as though nothing had ever happened!

The postnatal period is a time of recovery. We need time to restore physically and to adjust mentally. Our baby depends and thrives upon our well-being. Cultures globally recognise this and have designed rituals to aid our minds and bodies after birth. Cultural postnatal customs have been found to be generally beneficial by offering women space to recover from the exhaustion of childbirth.[101]

This may be because rituals are "a rite of passage, and a rite of passage marks the transition from one social role to another".[102] It is this rite of passage that cultures aim to ease and make welcoming, both for the mother and the baby. This aspect of rituals formulates the benefit in particular cultural norms associated with childbirth. There "must be a welcoming climax to the rite of passage, otherwise the participant is left high and dry, with feelings of alienation and distress".[103]

After nine months of waiting for this baby and to become a mother, the big day finally arrives. The excitement and preparation can end with a difficult time. After nine months of doting and attention, we disappear into the background as our baby takes the limelight. We need time to recover and to re-adjust. Being unable to do so has possible links with postnatal depression and delayed recovery. Once the adrenalin from labour and birth finally leaves

---

101 Vincent Priya, J. (1992), *Birth Traditions and Modern Pregnancy Care,* Element Books, Shaftesbury

102 Podolinski, J., Women's Experience of Postnatal Support, p 212 cited in *Psychological Perspectives on Pregnancy and Childbirth*, Clement, S. (ed) (1998) Edinburgh, Churchill Livingstone

103 *Ibid*

us many women often feel low, both physically and emotionally. It is common to have the "baby blues" and over one in twelve mothers suffer from postnatal depression (PND).[104,105] It is entirely normal to feel down after having a baby, even for many months to come. Our bodies undergo massive physical and hormonal change, our lives take on new angles and daily routine is no longer determined by us but by a little baby. Thus, it is important after birth to take it easy, eat and sleep well and look after ourselves, if not be looked after! The benefits of being mobile very soon after the birth, such as helping bowel movements, do not negate the need for rest and help.

However, there are some practices associated with the postnatal period that are best left as abandoned practices as they have no basis in Islam and are of no benefit to our babies, or to us. Take, for example, the taboo surrounding eclipses and pregnant women. Many cultures consider an eclipse to be bad luck, especially for pregnant women and their babies. In these cultures, pregnant women are told to remain indoors and not do anything, or to look to the sky during an eclipse for fear of having a spot or deformity in the child. There is no basis in Islam for this.

Sometimes cultural practices carry reasons, even good reasons, but at other times they are senseless or have become so due to time. In contrast, Allah ﷻ has made His religion easy and His laws are timeless. They will always carry wisdom and therefore all that contradicts His laws, including prevailing cultural beliefs, must be set aside. Any cultural practices that do not require compromising

104 There is a free information booklet on postnatal depression. This is available online at: www.mind.org.uk/NR/rdonlyres/7ED23EFA-B7E4-4D47-8DF5-1B793F3FB143/0/Understanding_postnatal_depression.pdf

105 Gaynes, B. N., et al. (2005), Perinatal depression: prevalence, screening, accuracy, and screening outcomes - Summary, Evidence Report/Technology Assessment No. 119, AHRQ Publication No. 05-E0006-1. Rockville, MD, Agency for Healthcare Research and Quality

on Allah's ﷻ laws can be considered and it is up to the individual whether or not to leave it, depending on the perceived benefits. For example, we can choose to avoid certain foods as Allah ﷻ or His Prophet ﷺ do not speak of any recommendations or constraints regarding food during this time, just as long as we do not go to the extent of making them *haram* upon ourselves as it is only Allah ﷻ who determines what is *halal* and *haram* for us.

Some common misconceptions regarding the postnatal period include the following:

1. *Nifas* is forty days for everyone

Nifas, or postnatal bleeding, does not always last forty days. The length of *nifas* differs for each woman and even for each pregnancy for the same woman. If we stop bleeding before forty days we must resume prayer, fasting and our relationships in full with our husbands. If we do not bleed for a full forty days then we cannot continue to leave these obligations. We must also ensure that we begin praying again and so on if we continue to bleed beyond the maximum days of *nifas* as Allah ﷻ has prescribed a cut-off period for *nifas*. According to Imams Abu Hanifa and Hanbal, this is forty days and Imams Shafi'i and Malik state the maximum period for *nifas* to be sixty days.

2. The postnatal woman and newborn are unclean and everything in contact with them is also unclean

Nifas does not render a woman a despised being. She is in a state similar to menstruation or as one would be after sexual intercourse. There is no need to wash the house, curtains and carpets included, after we stop bleeding as we are not filthy! The absence of purity applies to the woman only, and only in relation to acts of worship and relations with her husband, not everything she has breathed on!

On a similar note, there is no need to bathe the baby and undertake any special rituals or rites to purify the baby once it is forty days old. The bathing and purification mark the end of *nifas* for the mother, whenever she stops bleeding, even if that is within forty days. There is no basis for special cleansing for the baby to coincide with the mother leaving *nifas*.

3. The postnatal woman must remain indoors

We *are* allowed to leave our house when in *nifas*. Indeed, Allah سبحانه وتعالى asks of us not to be out of our homes unnecessarily, whether we are new mums or not as He says:

> *And stay in your houses, and make not a dazzling display, like that of the former Times of Ignorance.* (Surah Al-Ahzab 33:33)

However, for the postnatal mother, some cultures dictate that we should not leave the house. Most women have hospital births and so they are already out of the house anyway! To hold the belief that a postnatal woman must not leave her home is incorrect. So if we have to go and buy nappies then we can happily do so!

Sure, we are likely to be tired and very busy and might not want to, or need to, leave the house, which is also fine. Many women take pleasure in being at home with their brand new babies, voluntarily not leaving the house very much, if at all. This is not due to cultural norms or pressures but simply to adjust to motherhood and recover, accommodating for the tiny new being we so eagerly awaited. The postnatal period, like pregnancy, is a special time as it is only these first few weeks of our babies' lives that they are newborns. A collection of memorable first nappy changes and feeds unfold and the foundations of the unbreakable bonds of parent and baby begin. This is a time we can never bring back so let's enjoy it!

A New Life Begins

The birth of our precious new baby marks the end of the beautiful days of pregnancy. Most women are itching (sometimes literally!) to give birth and to leave the discomforts of carrying their baby. Often, like all good things in life, it is only when the bliss of pregnancy has passed us by that we realise what a joy and mercy it had been. The feeling of the baby moving inside us, listening to their heartbeat, imagining holding them and shopping for a newborn we cannot wait to meet is all to be missed!

Undoubtedly, beginning motherhood also has its delights; there is no feeling comparable to the day we see and hold a brand new baby. These pleasures outweigh many of the perks of pregnancy by far. However, together with the bliss of a newborn baby, life as a brand new mum can often be challenging. We all know that it is far easier looking after a baby that is cosily tucked in our womb rather than a newborn that needs reassurance, feeding and changing! It is not only the baby that begins a new life, so do we.

Many new mothers spend the first nights with their newborn simply awed by the baby they have just given birth to. We can spend hours lying awake, just looking at them as they sleep peacefully. Everyone believes motherhood is a smooth transition that all women make and that it must all be wonderful. However, many new mothers feel they are not being the best of mothers and are falling short of their own expectations. After having a baby, the weight of the responsibility of motherhood can often seem like the be-all and end-all of life. It is important to remember that, despite our responsibilities to our babies, there is more to life because we have to maintain our own striving too:

> *O you who believe! Let not your wealth, or your children, divert you from the remembrance of Allah; and whoever does that, these are the losers.* (Surah Al-Munafiqun 63:9)

In maintaining our faith we ensure a focus on our own character, our relationship with Allah ﷻ, and with other people. It benefits our baby and our ability as a mother in countless ways to keep this correct perspective. Bear in mind that our number one priority is the remembrance of Allah ﷻ. Our children should not be a distraction from this.

Of course, children do not have to be the cause of distraction or destruction; rather, they will *insha'Allah* be a door to *Jannah*. Children are a unique bounty as they are one of only three things that can continue to benefit us after we die:

> When a man dies, accrual of merit in his favour from good deeds ceases except from three actions: charity which continues after his death, knowledge left behind from which men continue to benefit and righteous offspring who pray for him. *(Muslim, Book of Bequests)*

In addition, *insha'Allah*, the good we receive through our babies is one that does not cease when we do.

> A man will be raised some degrees in Paradise and he will say, "For what reason am I receiving this?" He will be told, "Because of your son asking forgiveness for you." *(Muslim, Book of Bequests)*

Imagine the bliss of attaining *Jannah* and then having an added surprise of a position higher than expected! This we can await if we raise our children to remember us and seek forgiveness for us. It can be powerful fuel, particularly during trying times, to remind ourselves that every effort for our baby can be a source of such great happiness on the Day we meet our Lord, if we raise them for His sake. Such aspirations form the foundations of the intentions that we must have now, at the beginning of our journey of motherhood. We thank Allah ﷻ for this wonderful opportunity to multiply our good deeds with every single day that we have with our children.

May He make us amongst the best of mothers and grant us amongst the best of children. *Ameen.*

Appendix

i) Du'as for You

Khushoo'

اللَّهُمَّ إِنِّي أَعُوْذُ بِكَ مِنْ قَلْبٍ لاَ يَخْشَى

Allahumma innee a'udhu bika min qalbin la yakhsha
"O Allah, I seek refuge with You from a heart that has no *khushoo'*." *(Tirmidhi)*

Whilst in *Sajda*

اللَّهُمَّ اغفِرْ لِي ذَنْبِي كُلَّهُ دِقَّهُ وَجِلَّهُ

Allahum-maghfir lee dhanbee kullahu diqqahu wa jillahu
"O Allah, forgive me my sins, the minor and the major." *(Muslim)*

When in *Ruku*

سُبْــحَانَ رَبِّــيَ الْعَظِــيْمِ

Subhana Rabbi al-'Adheem (3 times)
Glory be to my Supreme Lord *(Abu Dawud and others)*

سُبــوْحٌ قُــدُّوْسٌ، رَبُّ الْمَلاَئِكَــةِ وَالــرُّوْحِ

Subbuhun, Quddusun, Rabbul-mala'ikati war-ruh
Perfect, Blessed, Lord of the Angels and the Spirit. *(Muslim, Abu Dawud)*

After *Ruku*

سَمِــعَ اللهُ لِمَــنْ حَمِــدَهُ

Sami' Allahu liman hamidah
Allah hears whoever praises Him. *(Bukhari)*

رَبَّنَــا وَلَكَ الحَمْــدُ حَمْــداً كَثِــيْراً طَيِّــباً مُــبَارَكاً فِيْهِ

Rabbana wa laka'l-hamdu hamdan katheeran tayyiban mubarakan fih
Our Lord to You be much good and blessed praise. *(Bukhari)*

Good character

اِهْدِنِي لِأَحْسَنِ الْأَخْلَاقِ لاَ يَهْدِي لِأَحْسَنِهَا إِلاَّ أَنْتَ

Ihdini li ahsanil akhlaqi la yahdi li ahsaniha illa anta
"Guide me to good character, none guides to good character but You." *(Muslim)*

Gratitude

اللَّهُمَّ أَعِنِّي عَلَى ذِكْرِكَ وَشُكْرِكَ وَحُسْنِ عِبَادَتِكَ

Allahumma a'innee ala dhikrika wa shukrika wa husni ibadatika
"O Allah, help me to remember You and to give thanks to You and to worship You well." *(Ahmad, Tirmidhi)*

Putting on Clothes

اَلْحَمْدُ لِلَّهِ الَّذِي كَسَانِي هذَا (الثَّوب) وَرَزَقَنِيهِ
مِنْ غَـيْـرِ حَولٍ مِنِّي وَلاَ قُـوَّةٍ

Alhamdu lillahil ladhee kasanee hatha (ath-thowba) wa razaqneehi min ghairi hawlin minnee wa la quwwatin

"All praise is for Allah who has clothed me with this (garment) and provided it for me, with no power nor might from myself." *(Bukhari)*

Looking in the Mirror

الْحَمْدُ لِلَّهِ اللَّهُمَّ كَمَا حَسَّنْتَ خَلْقِي فَحَسِّنْ خُلُقِي

Alhamdu lillahi allahumma kama hassanta khalqi fahassin khuluqi

"All praises are due to Allah, O Allah, as you have given me a good physical form, so also favour me with good morals and manners." *(Al-Nasai)*

Alleviating Stress

اللَّهُمَّ إِنِّي أَعُوذُ بِكَ مِنَ الْهَمِّ وَالْحَزَنِ، وَالْعجْزِ وَالْكَسَلِ، وَالْبُخْلِ وَالْجُبْنِ،
وَضَلَعِ الدَّيْنِ، وَغَلَبَةِ الرِّجَالِ.

Allahumma innee a'udhu bika minal hammi walhazani, wal ajzi wal kasali, wal bukhli wal jubni, wa dhala'id dayni, wa ghalabatir rijali

"O Allah, I seek refuge with You from distress, grief, incapacity, laziness, miserliness, cowardice, the burden of debt and from being overpowered by men." *(Bukhari)*

اللَّهُمَّ إِنِّي عَبْدُكَ وَابْنُ عَبْدِكَ وَابْنُ أَمَتِكَ نَاصِيَتِي بِيَدِكَ مَاضٍ فِيَّ حُكْمُكَ عَدْلٌ فِيَّ قَضَاؤُكَ أَسْأَلُكَ بِكُلِّ اسْمٍ هُوَ لَكَ سَمَّيْتَ بِهِ نَفْسَكَ أَوْ عَلَّمْتَهُ أَحَدًا مِنْ خَلْقِكَ أَوْ أَنْزَلْتَهُ فِي كِتَابِكَ أَوِ اسْتَأْثَرْتَ بِهِ فِي عِلْمِ الْغَيْبِ عِنْدَكَ أَنْ تَجْعَلَ الْقُرْآنَ رَبِيْعَ قَلْبِي وَ نُورَ صَدْرِي وَجَلَاءَ حُزْنِي وَذَهَابَ هَمِّي

Allahumma innee 'abduka wabnu 'abdika wabnu amatika nasiyatee biyadika madhin fiyya hukmuka 'adlun fiyya qadhauka asaluka bikulli ismin huwa laka sammayta bihi nafsaka aw 'allamtahu ahadan min khalqika aw anzaltahu fee kitabika aw-ista'tharta bihi fee 'ilmil ghaibi 'indaka an taj'alal quraana rabi'a qalbee wa noora sadree wa jalaa-a huznee wa dhahaba hammee

"O Allah, I am Your slave, son of Your slave, son of Your maidservant; my forelock is in Your hand, Your command over me is forever executed and Your decree over me is just. I ask You by every name belonging to You which You have named Yourself with, or revealed in Your Book, or You taught to any of Your creation, or You have preserved in the knowledge of the Unseen with You, that You make the Qur'an the life of my heart and the light of my breast, and a departure for my sorrow and a release for my anxiety." *(Ahmad)*

اللَّهُمَّ رَحْمَتَكَ أَرْجُو فَلَا تَكِلْنِي إِلَى نَفْسِي طَرْفَةَ عَيْنٍ،
وَأَصْلِحْ لِي شَأْنِي كُلَّهُ لَا إِلَهَ إِلَّا أَنْتَ

Allahumma rahmataka arjoo falaa takilnee ila nafsee tarfata 'ain, wa aslih lee sha'nee kullahu la illa ha illa anta

"O Allah, for Your mercy I hope, so do not leave me in charge of my affairs even for the blink of an eye; rectify all my affairs. There is no god except You." *(Al-Hakim)*

ii) Du'as for Baby

Before Intercourse

بِاسْمِ اللَّهِ، اللَّهُمَّ جَنِّبْنَا الشَّيْطَانَ، وَجَنِّبِ الشَّيْطَانَ مَا رَزَقْتَنَا

Bismillahi, Allahumma jannibna-shaytana, wa jannibi-shaytana ma razaqtana

"In the name of Allah. O Allah, keep us away from *Shaytan* and keep *Shaytan* away from what You provide us." *(Bukhari)*

Du'a for a Righteous Soul

رَبِّ هَبْ لِي مِن لَّدُنْكَ ذُرِّيَّةً طَيِّبَةً إِنَّكَ سَمِيعُ الدُّعَاءِ

Rabbi hablee mil-ladunka dhurriyyatan tayyibatan innaka samee'ud du'a

"O my Lord! Grant me from You a good offspring. You are indeed the All-Hearer of invocation." (Surah Al-'Imran 3: part of verse 38)

رَبِّ هَبْ لِي مِنَ الصَّالِحِينَ

Rabbi hablee min-as saliheen

"My Lord! Grant me (offspring) from the righteous." (Surah As-Saffat 37:100)

Protection from Evil

إِنِّي أُعِيذُهَا بِكَ وَذُرِّيَّتَهَا مِنَ الشَّيْطَانِ الرَّجِيمِ

Innee u'eedhuha bika wa dhur-riyyataha min-ash shaytanir rajeem

"I seek refuge with You for her and for her offspring from the outcast *Shaytan.*" (Surah Al-'Imran 3: end of verse 36)

أَعُوذُ بِكَلِمَاتِ اللَّهِ التَّامَّةِ مِنْ كُلِّ شَيْطَانٍ وَهَامَّةٍ وَمِنْ كُلِّ عَيْنٍ لاَمَّةٍ

A'udhu bikalimatil lahit-tammati min kulli shaytanin wa ham-matin wa min kulli 'ainin lammah

"O Allah! I seek refuge with Your Perfect Words from every devil and from poisonous pests and from every evil, harmful, envious eye." *(Bukhari)*

قُلْ أَعُوذُ بِرَبِّ الْفَلَقِ. مِنْ شَرِّ مَا خَلَقَ. وَمِنْ شَرِّ غَاسِقٍ إِذَا وَقَبَ. وَمِنْ شَرِّ النَّفَّاثَاتِ فِي الْعُقَدِ. وَمِنْ شَرِّ حَاسِدٍ إِذَا حَسَدَ.

Qul a'udhu bi rabbil falaq. Min sharri ma khalaq. Wa min sharri ghasiqin idha waqab. Wa min sharrin naffathati fil uqad. Wa min sharri hasiddin idha hasad.

"Say: I seek refuge with the Lord of the Dawn. From the mischief of created things; From the mischief of Darkness as it overspreads; From the mischief of those who practise secret arts; And from the mischief of the envious one as he practises envy. And from the evil of the envier when he envies." (Surah Al-Falaq 113)

iii) Du'a in Labour

اللَّهُمَّ لاَ سَهْلَ إِلاَّ مَا جَعَلْتَهُ سَهْلاً

Allahumma la sahla illa ma ja'altahu sahlan...
O Allah, there is nothing easy except what You make easy...

وَ أَنْتَ تَجْعَلُ الْحَزْنَ إِذَا شِئْتَ سَهْلاً

...wa 'anta taja'lu-l-hazna 'idha shi'ta sahlan.
...And you can make grief, if You wish, easy. *(Ibn al Sunni)*

يَا حَيُّ ، يَا قَيُّومُ ، بِرَحْمَتِكَ أَسْتَغِيثُ

Ya Hayyu, ya Qayyumu, bi-rahmatika astaghithu
O the Living, O the Eternal, I seek help in Your grace. *(Tirmidhi)*

اللَّهُمَّ رَحْمَتَكَ أَرْجُو فَلاَ تَكِلْنِي إِلَى نَفْسِي طَرْفَةَ عَيْنٍ، وَ أَصْلِحْلِي شَأْنِي كُلَّهُ لاَ إِلَهَ إِلاَّ أَنْتَ

Allahumma rahmataka arju, fala takilnee ila nafsee tarfata'ain, wa aslihlee sha'nee kullahu, la ilaha illa anta
O Allah, I hope for Your mercy, so give me not over to myself even for as little as the wink of an eye, and set right all my affairs, there is no god but You. *(Abu Dawud)*

اللَّهُ اللَّهُ رَبِّي لاَ أُشْرِكُ بِهِ شَيْئًا

Allah, Allah, Rabbi la ushriku bihi shay-an
Allah, Allah, my Lord, I associate none with Him. *(Tirmidhi)*

لاَ إِلَهَ إِلاَّ أَنْتَ سُبْحَانَكَ إِنِّي كُنتُ مِنَ الظَّالِمِينَ.

La ilaha illa anta, subhanaka, innee kuntu minadh-dhalimin
There is no god but You, You are far exalted and above all weaknesses, and I was indeed the wrongdoer. (Surah Yunus 10: part of verse 87)

اللَّهُمَّ إِنِّي عَبْدُكَ ، ابْنُ عَبْدِكَ ، ابْنُ أَمَتِكَ ، نَاصِيَتِي بِيَدِكَ ، مَاضٍ فِيَّ حُكْمُكَ، عَدْلٌ فِيَّ قَضَاؤُكَ ، أَسْأَلُكَ بِكُلِّ اسْمٍ هُوَ لَكَ ، سَمَّيْتَ بِهِ نَفْسَكَ ، أَوْ أَنْزَلْتَهُ فِي كِتَابِكَ ، أَوْ عَلَّمْتَهُ أَحَدًا مِنْ خَلْقِكَ أَوِ اسْتَأْثَرْتَ بِهِ فِي عِلْمِ الْغَيْبِ عِنْدَكَ ، أَنْ تَجْعَلَ الْقُرْآنَ رَبِيعَ قَلْبِي ، وَ نُورَ صَدْرِي ، وَ جَلاَءَ حُزْنِي ، وَ ذَهَابَ هَمِّي

Allahumma innee 'abduka wabnu 'abdika wabnu amatika nasiyatee biyadika madhin fiyya hukmuka 'adlun fiyya qadha-uka asaluka bikulli ismin huwa laka sam-mayta bihi nafsaka aw 'allamtuhu ahadan min khalqika aw anzaltahu fee kitabika aw-ista'tharta bihi fee 'ilmil ghaibi 'indaka an taj'alal quraana rabi'a qalbee wa noora sadree wa jalaa-a huznee wa thahaba hammee
O Allah, I am Your servant, son of Your servant, son of your maidservant. My forehead is in Your hand. Your command concerning me prevails, and Your decision concerning me is just. I call upon You by every one

of the beautiful names by which You have described Yourself, or which You have revealed in Your book, or have taught anyone of Your creatures, or which You have chosen to keep in the knowledge of the unseen with You, to make the Qur'an the delight of my heart, the light of my breast, and remover of my grief, sorrows, and afflictions. *(Ahmad and Ibn Hibban)*

إِنَّا لِلَّهِ وَإِنَّا إِلَيْهِ رَاجِعُوْنَ

Inna lillah wa inna ilayhi raaji'oon
To Allah we belong, and to Him is our return (Surah Al-Baqarah 2:part of verse 156)

اللَّهُمَّ أَجِرْنِي فِيَّ مُصِيبَتِي وَاخْلَفْ لِي خَيْرًا مِنْهَا

Allahumma ajirnee fee musibatee wakhlafli khairan minha
Oh, Allah, help me through my ordeal and grant me better than it after. *(Muslim)*

رَبِّ إِنِّي لِمَا أَنزَلْتَ إِلَيَّ مِنْ خَيْرٍ فَقِير

Rabbi innee lima anzalta ilayya min khairin faqeer
O my Lord! I am indeed needy of whatever good You may send to me. (Surah Al-Qasas: 24)

Index

Other related books published by Ta-Ha Publishers Ltd.:

The Greatest Gift: A Guide to Parenting
by Muhammad Abdul Bari

Marriage and Family Building in Islam
by Muhammad Abdul Bari

The Muslim Woman's Handbook
by Huda Khattab

Please visit **www.taha.co.uk** *for more details*